Teach-Stat
Activities

**Statistical Investigations
for Grades 1 Through 3**

STATISTICS:
A Key to
Better Mathematics

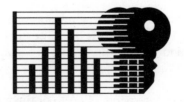

**The University of North Carolina
Mathematics and Science Education Network**

Dale Seymour Publications®

Project Editor: Joan Gideon
Production Coordinator: Claire Flaherty
Composition: Andrea Reider
Art: Carl Yoshihara
Cover Design: Don Taka
Cover Illustration: Terry Guyer

Published by Dale Seymour Publications®, an imprint of
the Alternative Publishing Group of Addison-Wesley Publishing Company.

The Teach-Stat materials were prepared with the support of National
Science Foundation Grant No. TPE-9153779. Any opinions, findings,
conclusions, or recommendations expressed in this publication are
those of the authors and do not necessarily represent the views of the
National Science Foundation. These materials shall be subject to a royalty-free,
irrevocable, worldwide, nonexclusive license in the United States Government
to reproduce, perform, translate, and otherwise use and to authorize others
to use such materials for government purposes.

 This project was supported, in part,
by the
National Science Foundation
Opinions expressed are those of the authors
and not necessarily those of the Foundation

Additional funding was provided by the North Carolina Department of
Public Instruction and the North Carolina Statewide Systemic Initiative.

Order Number DS21408
ISBN 0-86651-951-3

1 2 3 4 5 6 7 8 9 10-ML-00 99 98 97 96

DALE
SEYMOUR
PUBLICATIONS®
P.O. BOX 10888
PALO ALTO, CA 94303

This book is printed
on recycled paper.

Year One Teachers

Irene Baldwin
T. J. Blake
Carol Blankenhorn
Anessa Burgman
SuAnn Burton
Cynthia Collins
Elaine Corbett
Lisa Ann Crocker
Mary Lee Danielson
Rita Davis
Rebecca Deal
Ann Diedrick
Barbara Dishman
Doris Farmer
Marie Flynt
Mary Anne Simon Frost
Robin Frost
Sue Ellen Goldstein
Barbara Ann Gustafson
Eileen Hartwell
Donna Hash
Angela Heustess
Deborah Hill
Mary Ann Hopkins
Carla Jacobs
Donna James
Donna Jenkins
Denise Jewell
Sharon Frances Leak Jones
Rosemary Klein
Cathy Jo Korenek
Gail Lane
Jacqueline Lauve
Linda Law
Sharon Leonard
Charisma Lindberg
Amy Loy
Ron Luciano
Rhonda McCurry
Kay Moore
Phyllis Moore
Teresa Pace
Wendy Rich
Paula Rigsbee
Paula Segers
Linda South
Linda Stroupe
Sandra Styron
Frances Toledano
Cheryl Varner

Jane Wagner
Harriet Weinstock
Anne White
Deborah Whorley
Julia Wilkie
Sheila Wilkins
Vicki Yoder

Year Two Teachers

Pat Adkisson
Sandra Albarty
Etta Alston
Donna Anderson
Mary Backes
Brenda Bailey
Kathy Baily
Debra Baize
Lisa Baker
Rosemary Barker
Jennie Beedle
Kim Beeson
Cynthia Bell
Brenda Berry
Suzanne Billips
Sandra Billups
Martha Blount
Charles Brantley
Kimberly Briles
Hilda Bukowski
Barbara Burns
Gregg Byrum
Hattie Campbell
Angela Cannon
Ann Cannon
Mariea Carey
Bennie Carpenter
Alissa Carver
Evelyn Case
Lisa Celotto
Betsy Church
Leticia Clark
Sue Clayton
Nancy Cooke
Marsha Corbett
William Cornett
Beth Cornwell
Bettie Council
Susan Creasy
Janice Croasmun
Pamela Crowhurst

Becky Crump
Dinah Cuthbertson
Carol Davidson
Judy Davidson
Debra Davis
Sylvia Davis
Ann Dawson
Patricia Denson
Susan Douglas
Terry Dryman
Donna Dysert
Roberta Ebron
Donna Edmiston
Ruth Ann Edmunds
Barbara Elder
Angela Farrar
Brookie Ferguson
Diane Flagler
Jennifer Flesca
Bonnie Flynn
Phyllis Forbes
Judy Foster
Dorothy Freeman
Jennifer Freeman
Denise Fuller
Marcia Gallant
Debra Gandy
Barbara Gaw
Angela Gaylor
Nancy Glenham
Joan Goff
Clarke Goodman
Phillip Gordon
Beth Graves
Maria Grigg
Sarah Gustafson
Lisa Haley
Greg Hathcock
Cheryl Hawkins
Katherine Hayes
Catherine Heglar
Montrose Helms
Susan Henderson
Lisa Henningan
Annie Hicks
Helen Hollis
Patty Honeycutt
Sharyn Hoover
Gail Horne
Janice House
Amanda Hykin
Barbara Jackson

Jo Johnson
Sandy Johnson
Julie Jones
Lois Jones
Sandra Jones
Carolyn Joplin
Saralyn Kader
Julie Kappers
Margaret Kelder
Virginia Kelly
Frances Kemp
Betsy Kinlaw
Becky Kirkendall
Irene Koonce
Flora Annette Kremer
Jeanne Lamb
Vivian Lamm
Benita Lawrence
Karen Lawrence
Addie Leggett
Mary Lipscomb
Diane Livingston
Leah Lowry
Margaret Lundy
Lorraine Malphurs
Donald Mapson
Camille Marlowe
Grace Martin
Nancy Martin
Cathi McClain
Margaret Anne McColl
Debbie McCord
Virginia McElroy
Diane McFerrin
Donald Rose McGhee
Kitty McGimsey
Dorothy Gray McKoy
Tina McSwain
Clyde Melton
Kathy Mizerak
Jackie Monroe
Barbara Moore
Louise Moore
Linda Moose
Aundra Moretz
Mary Morrow
Pat Mullens
Michael Mulligan
Karen Myers
Cheryl Newby
Debra O'Neal
Brenda Oxford

Shelia Page
Karen Parham
Cynthia Parker
Barbara Paul
Deborah Pevatte
Janice Phillips
Keyna Pittman
Molly Pope
Betty Powell
Jane Powell
Kim Berry Price
Donese Pulley
Virginia Reed
Cheryl Ricks
Charlotte Riddick
Carla Rierson
Karen Rodenhizer
Deborah Ross
Lynne S. Rozier
Barbara Seaforth
Ramona Sethill
Jacqueline Setliff
Barbara Shafer
Jean Slate
Cynthia Smith
Jean M. Smith
Pamela Smith
Susan Parker Smith
Terry Smith
Stephen Sorrell
Joan Stafford
Brenda Stanley
Polly Stewart
Wanda Sutton
Judy Swain
Betty Sykes
Katherine Taylor
Janet Thompson
Kimberly Thompson
C. Henry Thorne
Debbie Thorsen
Jennifer Tilley
Allene Trachte
Kathy Tramble
Carolyn Tryon
Gail Uldricks
Mary Clay Vick
Carol Wainwright
Linda Ward
James R. Watson
Priscilla Waycaster
Doris Weaver

Glenda Weaver
Sarah Wells
Patsy Whitby
Susan Whitehurst
Joseph N. Whitley, Jr.
Harriette Whitlow
Peggy Lee Wilder
Hollis Williams
Judy Williams
Wanda Williams
Myrtle Winstead
Jacequelin Wiseman
Brenda Woodruff
Kimberly Woodruff
Linda Wright
June Zurface

Contents

Introduction to
Teach-Stat Activities

Children live in a world of numbers. They ask for three cookies; they count six steps as they walk up or down stairs; they compare how many toys they have with how many their friends have. In the primary years children learn to read, recognize, and write numbers. They begin to record their ideas on paper. They become more adept at solving problems, making conjectures, and drawing conclusions. They start to discuss their reasoning and to make connections among ideas. They begin to develop their data sense.

The development of data sense encompasses much of what youngsters experience and learn in their primary years: they develop language skills; they explore and become adept at using different counting strategies; and they investigate size, shape, and number. Gradually, they develop an understanding of our place-value system.

Children's natural curiosity leads them to ask many questions, and their increasing vocabulary allows them to describe details and to make comparisons: *more than, less than, the same as, different from.* They gradually come to understand the symbolic representations of ideas. They become confident in using numbers and data displays to describe things in the world around them.

Statistics, once an advanced area of study, has become an integral part of the K–12 curriculum. The *Curriculum and Evaluation Standards for School Mathematics* (NCTM 1989) calls for students at the K–4 level to have experiences with data analysis and probability so that students can

- collect, organize, and describe data
- construct, read, and interpret displays of data
- formulate and solve problems that involve collecting and analyzing data
- explore concepts of chance

Developing data sense is part of becoming mathematically powerful. Much of the data students encounter are inconclusive or conflicting. They need to develop skill in finding information, and in interpreting and using data to answer questions and to make decisions.

A classroom in which students are able to investigate their own how and why questions provides a rich environment for building self-confidence and constructing fundamental understandings about data. Through investigations, young students learn to pose more and more precise questions in their quest for answers. They learn different ways to collect and organize data. Because they are the researchers, children have ownership of the information they gather. Representing information in a variety of formats gives them experience in making decisions and communicating mathematically. They learn to analyze their data and to interpret their results with respect to their original questions.

Data investigations allow children to answer questions that are not immediately obvious. The teacher, too, may discover answers not known before the investigations.

About This Book

This book contains classroom activities used by teachers across North Carolina in a project called Teach-Stat: A Key to Better Mathematics. Funded by the National Science Foundation, Teach-Stat includes a professional-development curriculum for workshops for elementary teachers and a curriculum for institutes to develop elementary statistics educators who can lead staff development for colleagues. Through the project, teachers learn more about statistics and ways to integrate the teaching of statistics into their classroom instruction.

Teach-Stat is two programs in one: a professional-development program for teachers of grades 1–6 and a staff-development program. It is designed to assist teachers in helping their students to develop data sense. The Teach-Stat program consists of three other related publications: *Teach-Stat for Teachers: Professional Development Manual* is a how-to guide for giving a three-week professional-development workshop to teachers of grades 1–6. Each activity emphasizes the components of the statistical-investigation process and related statistical concepts. *Teach-Stat for Statistics Educators: Staff Developers Manual* is a how-to guide for giving a one-week staff-development institute designed to prepare teachers to serve as resource people who can offer the Teach-Stat program to other teachers. *Teach-Stat Activities: Investigations for Grades 3–6* is a how-to guide for developing student activities in grades 3–6.

The activities in this book are organized into three sections. Activities 1–5, in the section *How Do Numbers Help Us Know Things?*, are designed to help students use sorting and counting to organize information. Activities 6–10, in the section *How Are We Alike or Different?*, offer students an opportunity to actually create data and organize it. Activities 11–15, in the section *What Do We Think?*, offer opportunities for students to use data to find out about themselves.

Each activity in this book has been used at several grade levels. For younger students, sometimes a very concrete means of displaying data by using real objects is most useful. For example, after a class discussion about attributes of their stuffed animals, students placed their stuffed toys on the floor in a graphing activity. Older children could use pictures of their animals, the names of their stuffed animals on cards, or their own pictures. At different times and for different groups of children, concrete, pictorial, and symbolic (abstract) representations of data will be appropriate. What is consistent throughout the activities is that the *data are meaningful to students and the various ways of recording data are appropriate to students' experiences.*

The Process of Statistical Investigation

The Teach-Stat activities follow a four-stage model—the PCAI model (Graham 1987)—for statistical investigations:

- *Pose the question* Identify a specific question to explore, and decide what data to collect to address the question.
- *Collect the data* Decide how to collect the data, and collect the data.
- *Analyze the data* Organize, summarize, describe, and display the data; and look for patterns in the data.
- *Interpret the results* Use the results from the analyses to make decisions about the original question.

The PCAI model gives structure and direction to the reasoning used in statistical problem solving. Individual components in the model are not necessarily self-contained, nor is the process always sequential. A fuller discussion of the model and a concept map of the process can be found in the section entitled the PCAI Model for Statistical Investigation (see page 95).

Getting Started

Each activity begins with some basic information and an overview that briefly describes the question being investigated and gives any special information you need before you begin. The "Mathematical Focus" lets you know about special emphases of the investigation, and the materials list alerts you to what you need to gather before beginning.

The heart of each activity is presented in four stages: Posing the Question, Collecting the Data, Analyzing the Data, and Interpreting the Data. There are ideas for variations throughout the investigations.

As you try these investigations with your students, you may have new experiences in your role as teacher. Teachers in the Teach-Stat project report that students sometimes initiate additional investigations even while they are involved in answering a question at hand. Shy children began to interact; outgoing students race in all directions with new questions to answer. Teachers became learners with their students. They are facilitators, posing additional "what if" questions and asking students to explain their conjectures and answers. They discover that the investigations connect content areas for a natural integration of curricula.

References

Curriculum and Evaluation Standards for School Mathematics. Reston, Virginia: National Council of Teachers of Mathematics, 1989.

Graham, A. *Statistical Investigations in the Secondary School.* Cambridge: Cambridge University Press, 1987.

Gleason, J., L. Vesiland, S. Friel, and J. Joyner. *Teach-Stat for Statistics Educators: Staff Developers Manual.* Palo Alto, California: Dale Seymour Publications, 1996.

Joyner, J., S. Pfeiffer, L. Vesiland, and S. Friel. *Teach-Stat Activities: Statistical Investigations for Grades 3–6.* Palo Alto, California: Dale Seymour Publications, 1997.

Friel, S., and J. Joyner. *Teach-Stat for Teachers: Professional Development Manual.* Palo Alto, California: Dale Seymour Publications, 1997.

What Are Our Favorite Stuffed Animals Like?

Mathematical Focus

- sorting and classifying
- comparing and ordering
- counting
- grouping
- collecting, organizing, and describing data
- creating real graphs and Venn diagrams
- predicting

Materials

- stuffed animal invitation (1 per child)
- children's stuffed animals
- teacher's stuffed animal
- extra stuffed animals
- name tags
- chart paper (optional)
- about 5 sorting circles (large loops of yarn or plastic hoops)
- sentence strips
- graphing mats (see "How to Make Graphing Mats")
- sheets of newsprint (in different sizes)
- crayons

Connections

Science
- sorting by single attributes, an introduction to keying
- exploring life science

Literature
- *The Velveteen Rabbit* by Margery Williams Bionco (Garden City, New York: Doubleday, 1922)
- *Corduroy* by Don Freeman (New York: Viking Press, 1968)
- *A Pocket for Corduroy* by Don Freeman (New York: Viking Press, 1978)
- *Ten Bears in My Bed* by Stan Mack (New York: Random House, 1974)
- *Ira Sleeps Over* by Bernard Waber (Boston: Houghton Mifflin, 1973)

Many children have well-loved stuffed animals that would "enjoy coming to school." In this investigation, children bring their stuffed animals to school. They can sort their animal friends by color, size, species, age, fuzziness, and other attributes. Ideally, categories for grouping and sorting will emerge from the children's own experience with their toys. The children then create real graphs using a variety of mats and pictorial approaches. This is a good investigation for early in the school year, because it creates a link between home and school.

Posing the Question

On the day before the children bring their stuffed animals to school, read a story about a stuffed animal. You might choose *The Velveteen Rabbit, Corduroy,* or *A Pocket for Corduroy.* After the story, ask the children if they have a stuffed animal at home. Encourage them to make some predictions about the different kinds of stuffed animals they have as a group and what their animals look like.

Which kind of stuffed animal do you think we have the most of? What color do you think most of our stuffed animals are? Do you think they are mostly new or mostly old? What else do you think we might find out when we bring our stuffed animals to school tomorrow?

Hand out copies of the invitations to the stuffed animals, which the children can show to their families. Explain that you will bring your own stuffed animal and several other animals for "adoption" by children who don't bring one from home.

On the next day, have the children make name tags for their stuffed animals, writing their own name on the back of the tags. The children may introduce their stuffed animals to the class, telling the animal's name, what kind of animal it is, and what is special about it.

Brainstorm with the children all the attributes they observe in the stuffed-animal collection, such as "furry" and "not furry," "clothes" and "no clothes," and "bears" and "not bears." Put this list on the board or chart paper for later use. Encourage the children to name categories that are not immediately obvious. For example:

Geri says her stuffed elephant is missing an eye. Does anyone else have an animal missing some part? How can we describe these animals?

From the Classroom

Several teachers who used this activity asked each child to hold up his or her animal as they wrote attributes on the board. This encouraged the children to focus on each attribute and allowed everyone to participate as the list was being made.

Sorting Circles

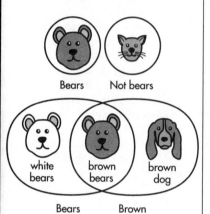

These sorting circles are called *Venn diagrams*. They are a way of showing how people, things, and ideas are related. Venn diagrams were named after John Venn (1834–1923), a mathematician whose specialty was logic.

What other questions can we ask about our animals? Let's make a list of things we might like to know. For example, we might ask "Where did we get our animals?" or "Do we sleep with our animals?"

Record all questions and suggestions.

Collecting the Data

The children collect data by sorting their stuffed animals. As an introduction to ordering data, have pairs of children compare the heights of their animals, then help groups of five or six use direct comparison to place their animals in a row from smallest (shortest) to largest (tallest).

Direct comparison is an early measurement skill, and it is the basis for ordering. This is a good opportunity to emphasize the vocabulary of comparison (such as *tall, taller, tallest, shortest, heavier*).

One of the questions someone asked was "Are most of our animals bears?" How can we find out? (Count them.) *Are there ways to make counting easier?*

When the children suggest that they can put all the bears together, lay two plastic hoops (or large circles of yarn) on the floor. Point to one of the rings.

Let's put all the bears inside this ring. What can we do with the animals that are not bears? (Put them in the other ring.)

Allow the children to place their animals in the rings.

What can we say about the animals in each ring? How many bears do we have?

Using attributes listed during the brainstorming session, have the children sort and resort their animals into other groups. Make labels for the rings as the children sort ("bears" and "not bears," "4 legs" and "2 legs"), adding pictures to the labels if necessary.

Can you think of any other ways we can sort our animals?

The children are likely to repeatedly suggest attributes that have several categories, such as color or size. Again, label the rings: "small animals," "medium animals," and "large animals." The children may suggest sorting by more than one attribute. For example, if the children suggest "bear" and "brown," write these labels, place one beside each ring, and then hold up a white bear.

Into which circle do we put this bear?

Next, hold up a brown animal other than a bear.

Where do we place this animal?

Now hold up a brown bear.

Where should we put this brown bear?

After the children realize that the brown bear belongs in both rings, ask them what they could do to correctly place the brown bear. The children will usually suggest adding a third ring with both labels or combining the two rings in some way. The children—or you—can demonstrate how to overlap the two rings (one labeled *brown* and one labeled *bear*) and place the animal that belongs in both rings in the intersection. This sorting process can be repeated for many attributes.

At this point, several additional activities can be explored to help the children focus on attributes. For example, put one stuffed animal by itself inside an unlabeled ring.

Who has an animal that might belong with this one? Why do you think so? [Mimi] put her animal with mine, because they are both [green]. Hers is a [dinosaur] and mine is a [frog], but they are the same color and that's why they can be together.

Teacher Note

It is often necessary to repeatedly ask, *"How are all of the animals alike? They all. . . ."* Children tend to separate individual objects in a group and explain, for example, "these are blue and these are round" rather than looking for one common attribute.

Parachute games in which the children sort themselves according to various attributes help them to recognize that attributes are the basis for grouping. *"Everyone who is wearing something red, run into the middle."* Or, *"Everyone who is wearing something red and something blue, run in."*

From the Classroom

In the fall of the school year, Judy Peede invited each of her grade 1 students to bring in a favorite stuffed animal. The class was involved in a unit on nighttime. Judy read *Ira Sleeps Over* to the class on the day the stuffed animals came to school, and the students wore their night clothes and turned day into night. Judy reported that they found many ways to sort and classify their stuffed animals. When they made a graph on the floor, they talked about how easy it was to count and compare the numbers of animals.

During the year, Judy's class made many other real graphs. In midwinter they investigated what color bow

they would want on a special present. Judy brought in red, green, blue, gold, and white stick-on bows, and each student chose the color he or she wanted. They created a real graph by sticking their bows onto a bulletin board display of large paper packages. Then Judy asked them to write about their special presents.

In the spring, the children explored favorite colors of plastic eggs by choosing their favorite egg from a large basket and placing it on a graphing mat. They decided to cut out paper eggs to match their plastic eggs and paste the paper eggs, with their names, on a graph to hang in the room. The class expanded their

investigation by gathering data from other classes. Teams of children visited each grade 1 class, taking the basket of eggs and a graphing mat to help them gather the data. The teams posed their question, then had students choose a favorite color egg and place it on the graphing mat. They recorded the responses from each class by counting out paper eggs of the same colors. Compiling data from all classes meant counting the paper eggs of each color. By stapling sets of five eggs together, they created a pictograph in which each pack of eggs represented five children. That year, blue was the favorite color egg!

Extension

Send a class stuffed animal home with one child at a time, along with a journal in which the children can draw or write about what happened at home. Helen Gore, a grade 1 teacher, found that family members also wrote in the journal. The class bear even took a trip to the beach, where its picture was taken playing in the sand. Before the end of the school year, this special bear had returned from weekend trips with a T-shirt and a pair of sunglasses.

Teacher Note

Sorting is the basis for creating *dichotomous keys*. Scientists sort plants and animals into groups by one attribute at a time. The stuffed animals can be divided into two groups—such as "bears" and "not bears"— giving the beginning of a dichotomous-key sort. Specific animals could be identified by moving one step at a time through the completed key—say, first "bear" and "not bear," then "large" and "small," then "light" and "dark." Anyone who has ever used a finder guide has used a dichotomous key. For example, consider *Tree Finder: A Manual for the Identification of Trees by Their Leaves* by May Theilgaard Watts (Berkeley, California: Nature Study Guild, 1991). You first select a typical leaf from the tree you wish to identify, then proceed step by step through the guide to identify the tree.

Does anyone else have an animal that belongs with ours? Can we put [Abby's brown puppy] with ours? Is there a way we could say all of our animals can belong together or are alike?

This exploration leads naturally into the game What's My Rule? Have the children put all of their animals in a group so that each animal can be seen. One child, the leader, thinks of an attribute and places several animals having that attribute in a ring. Other children take turns choosing an animal and placing it in the ring if they think it belongs with the other animals, outside the ring if they think it doesn't. The leader confirms or corrects each placement. After the children have placed several animals, they can try to guess the leader's attribute or sorting rule. If the children are having difficulty guessing the rule, the leader can offer them more clues by placing more animals with the correct attributes in the ring.

Mystery Animal is another game that allows children to communicate about attributes. The leader hides two or three animals in a large bag, then begins to name one of the animal's attributes. The other children try to guess which animal the leader is describing.

Analyzing the Data

Once the children have sorted the animals by an attribute, such as color or kind of animal, they can arrange them on square tiles on the floor or on graphing mats (see "How to Make Graphing Mats"). Labels can be used to describe what each column represents. Because larger animals take up more floor space than smaller animals, children will sometimes say there are more large animals, even when that is not true. Using a grid of squares with only one animal in each square will help the children make appropriate comparisons based on number.

When the children have placed all the animals on the grid, encourage them to talk about what they know about the animals.

What are some things we can say about our stuffed animals now? Do you notice some of the same things we mentioned when we put our animals in the rings?

As the children dictate, write sentence strips about the groups of animals (or have the children write their own sentences); for examples; "We have 8 bears." "We have 2 white bears and 6 brown bears." "We have 3 rabbits, 2 frogs, and 1 snake." "We have 18 animals with legs and 1 animal without legs." "We have 6 animals with a missing eye." "We have 7 hand-me-down animals, and they are all bears." Save the sentence strips to combine with the pictures the children draw of their animals and create a bulletin board display.

Teacher to Teacher

How to Make Graphing Mats

1. Slit a large plastic trash bag or clear lawn bag down one side and across the bottom, or slit the two sides and not the bottom. These two approaches will give you rectangles with different dimensions.

2. Open the bag.

3. Use masking tape or a permanent marker to make a grid of 6- to 10-inch squares.

Mats for creating real graphs can also be constructed from window shades, shower curtains, bed sheets, and vinyl yardage. Making real graphs first, and then recording the results with paper and pencil, helps children to connect their concrete experiences with more abstract representations. It's important to provide children with opportunities to bridge from concrete to abstract representations.

You may want to create several graphing mats of different-size squares for different purposes. For some activities, you may find that one mat isn't large enough and you need to place several side by side or end to end. There may be times when you want each child to have a personal mat. Create several blackline masters for yourself using different sizes of squares or rectangles. Having children create their own mats would provide them with opportunities to measure and use a ruler in a relevant situation.

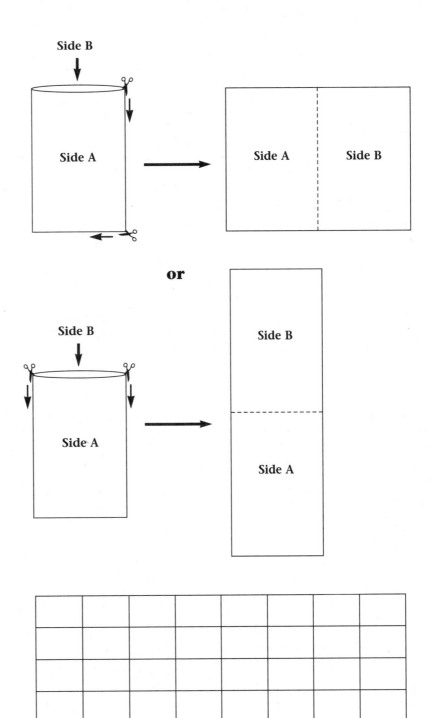

Fun Facts

The teddy bear was named after our twenty-sixth president, Theodore Roosevelt.

Let's make a big picture gallery of our animal friends so we can remember all these things about our animals. I want you all to draw and color your animal.

Place sheets of newspaper of different sizes on a table, and encourage the children to find the size that will best fit their stuffed animal.

Interpreting the Results

The children will have engaged in a great deal of discussion while sorting the stuffed animals. Take time to ask questions that encourage the children to reflect upon what they have learned.

Did anything surprise you about our stuffed animals? I wonder why there was only one [kangaroo]. I wonder why we have more [bears] than any other kind of stuffed animal.

If a new student came into our class tomorrow, what favorite stuffed animal do you think he or she would have? Why do you think this?

Have the children dictate, or write their own journal entries or letters, about what they have learned about the stuffed animals in the class.

A
Special
Invitation

To My
Favorite Stuffed Animal
You Are Invited to Attend School

_____
date or day

PLEASE COME IN A LARGE BAG FOR PROTECTION
LOVE, _____

P.S. *If you would rather not come to school, that's OK because I can adopt another stuffed animal for the day.*

How Did We Come to School Today?

Mathematical Focus

- sorting and classifying
- counting
- grouping
- collecting, organizing, and describing data
- creating picture graphs
- answering multiple questions using the same data

Materials

- index cards *(optional)*
- crayons
- copies of photographs of individual children *(optional)*
- sheets of chart paper *(one for each type of transportation)* or sorting circles *(yarn or plastic hoops)*
- sentence strips
- small pictures of modes of transportation *(optional; cut from "Modes of Transportation" sheet)*
- large pictures of modes of transportation *(optional)*
- glue or tape

Connections

Social Science
- exploring other cultures
- studying modes of transportation

Literature
- *Penelope Gets Wheels* by Esther Allen Peterson (New York: Crown, 1981)

At the beginning of the school year, an investigation about how students travel to school has high interest. The children draw from personal experience, so everyone is an expert on the topic!

The children begin by brainstorming ways they travel to school. Data can be gathered and displayed in several ways. Pictures of the children or their modes of transportation can be sorted into clusters or arranged in graphs. Representing the same data in different ways helps children to realize that the information remains the same even when the displays may look very different.

Posing the Question

What are all the different ways someone might get to school?

With the children, brainstorm answers to this question. Write each method on the board or sketch simple pictures, and label the collection "Ways to Get to School." You might want to talk about which ways are impractical in your area but would be important to students who live in other parts of the country or the world.

How did most of us come to school today?

Allow time for the children to express their opinions and explain their thinking. In the process, they may raise other questions. For example, they may want to know whether most of them came alone or with other children.

Do you ever change the way you come to school? Why? (because of a baby-sitter, or the weather)

At this point, consider taking time to read *Penelope Gets Wheels.*

Collecting the Data

Before they collect data, have the children make some kind of self-portrait. One approach is to have them draw a picture of themselves on index cards along with their names. Make sure everyone orients the card in the same direction.

Teacher Note

Using personal photographs when collecting data helps children identify with and own their data. Photograph each child, or photocopy the small pictures that accompany cumulative records; children can use them to make graphs throughout the year. If you mount pictures on card stock and laminate them, a small piece of magnetic tape turns them into a permanent graphing tool. Copies can also be glued onto a magnet or clothespin and used for taking attendance or counting meal choices as well as various sorting and graphing activities throughout the year.

Another approach is to duplicate small photographs of the children, such as those found on cumulative records. These can be pasted on grid paper and photocopied.

Instead of having the children draw pictures, you may want them to select from ready-made pictures such as buses, cars, feet, and bicycles (cut from the "Modes of Transportation" sheet) that represent how they got to school and write their names on the chosen picture. Help the children create pictures for options not given, such as a wheelchair.

How can we sort our pictures? For example, does anyone think we should put the cars and pick-up trucks in the same group? Why or why not?

Have the children sort their pictures on sheets of chart paper or in sorting circles created with lengths of yarn or plastic hoops, and ask them to name the categories. Overlap the rings to show somebody, for example, who traveled part of the way by walking and part of the way by bus.

Analyzing the Data

Once the children have decided on the categories and have sorted and resorted the pictures, encourage them to look at the whole display.

What does this show us about how we got to school? How many of us came to school by bus? How many of us walked? How did most of us get to school? If we put all the cars and trucks in the same group, would that change our answers? How?

Create a final display with pictures glued to large cutouts of each mode of transportation or onto a bar graph. Write sentence strips to describe the data. For example, "We came to school in 4 different ways," or "Most of us came on a bus."

If the children are ready to represent the data at a more abstract level, have them color in squares on graph paper to represent how they got to school.

Interpreting the Results

Ask questions to help the children begin reading the displays of data. It is important for them to recognize the one-to-one correspondence of children and pieces of data.

How many children are in each category? Which category has the most children? Which category has the least? Which categories have the same number of children?

Encourage the children to go beyond the factual information.

Do you think many of us live very close to school? Why do you say that? How long do you think it takes most of us to get to school? Why do you say that? Why do you think most of us came to school by [bus]?

If we lived in [a big city], do you think our groups would be the same or different?

If we compared our display to one made by students in the [eighth grade], do you think they would be the same?

If we asked this question in the [middle of the winter], would our display look the same? Why?

Encourage the children to use the same data to answer other questions.

How could we answer the question about whether most children came by themselves or with other children? How would we organize our pictures to find the answer to this question? Can you think of other ways to sort our pictures?

Displaying the same information in several ways gives young children opportunities to analyze and interpret familiar data.

If your class communicates with another class through the mail—electronic or otherwise—consider trading data with that class. Or, save the data to compare with next year's class or with data from students in other grades. If you use this investigation early in the year, save the data to compare it with data collected in a different season or at the end of the year.

From the Classroom

One grade 2 teacher found that his students were interested in how students get to school in other parts of the world. After researching this topic, his students were surprised to find so much variety in lifestyles and modes of transportation. They discovered that some students travel by horse, subway, snowmobile, and boat. Some even "travel" to school via computer and satellite hookups!

Teacher Note

The children may decide that their data does not supply enough information to answer all their questions, which might lead to collecting more data. The resulting discussion might be very rich in terms of what data tells us and doesn't tell us.

Modes of Transportation

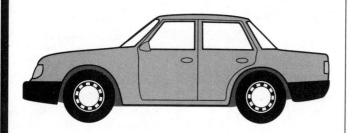

Car

Bus

Feet

Truck

Bicycle

Other

What Do We Have for Lunch?

Mathematical Focus

- counting and grouping
- collecting, organizing, and describing data
- creating bar graphs and tables
- problem solving

Materials

- cafeteria order forms *(if appropriate)*
- data-collection materials, including clothespins, magnets, and buttons

Connections

Science
- studying nutrition and the food pyramid

Literature
- *I Need a Lunch Box* by Jeannette Caines (New York: Harper Collins, 1993)
- *Bread and Jam for Frances* by Russell Hoban (New York: Harper Collins, 1986)
- *Smashed Potatoes: A Kid's-eye View of the Kitchen* edited by Jane G. Martel (Boston: Houghton Mifflin, 1974)
- *Moira's Birthday* by Robert Munsch (Toronto: Annick Press, 1987)
- *Sam's Sandwich* by David Pelham (New York: Dutton Children's Books, 1991)
- *Sam's Snack* by David Pelham (New York: Dutton Children's Books, 1994)

Numbers help us answer everyday questions, like how much pizza to cook or how many chocolate milks to order. "What Do We Have for Lunch?" can be adapted to fit your school's routine for counting and ordering lunches, thus making the activity relevant to children's lives. During this investigation, the children explore methods for collecting the information needed by the food-service staff when planning and preparing lunches. (If your school does not have food service, consider turning this investigation into "What Do We Bring for Lunch?")

Posing the Question

Questions about lunch orders are probably already part of your classroom routine. To provide the children with a richer frame of reference for this investigation, you may wish to arrange a visit to the school kitchen. Ask a cafeteria worker to explain how the classroom orders are used each day to order and prepare the food. This will help the children understand why this investigation is useful and how the questions asked in it are related to the real work of the cafeteria.

What do the cooks need to know from us? How do they use this information? Are they interested in how much each child will eat? How far in advance do they place orders for food and other things they need?

The question our cooks need answered today is "How many students want [pizza], and how many want [grilled cheese sandwiches]?"

(If your school cafeteria does not offer a choice of food, you may want to focus on the number of children who have a cafeteria lunch as opposed to those who bring their lunches.)

Collecting the Data

How does the way we collect lunch orders help give the cooks the information they need? What do we tell them about our lunch choices? How do we know who wants chocolate milk for lunch? Can this tell us how many people want plain milk?

Brainstorm a list of other ways to collect lunch orders. How the orders are collected will be influenced by whether or not you need to list individual students' names for certain choices. One teacher reported that she had to send the names of all students ordering

Consider inviting someone with a career in food service to speak to the class—such as a hospital nutritionist, a chef, a food editor, or a family cook (perhaps from one of the children's families). These role models can share information about their training and background, and how they use mathematics when planning, shopping, and cooking.

a baked potato to the cafeteria, because so many students changed their minds in the lunch line—taking potatoes because they didn't want the alternative—that many students who had ordered them didn't get them. If specific names aren't required, each child can place a token into a container or on a grid with the choices labeled.

You want the children to discover for themselves that their data-collection strategies must fit the questions they are trying to answer. As the children suggest ways to gather the information, you may wish to model some of their suggestions. For example, a child might suggest, "You could write my name and then ask me what I want and then write that next to my name. Then do that for Daniel, and for everyone else." You could demonstrate the collection method by asking several children for their order.

From the Classroom

One teacher shared that as her students arrive in the morning, each clips a clothespin marked with his or her name on a clothesline stretched across the wall. Pictures and names of lunch entrees are taped to the wall, and students put their clothespin near the entree they wish to order. (They do not have to order milk ahead of time; if students were to select an entree and a beverage, each would need two clothespins.)

Tammy Cullom reported that her class must order main entrees and vegetables because the lunches are delivered to the classroom. She uses a grid drawn on a metal board, and

magnetic buttons with students' names. The students learned quickly how to indicate their choices on the grid. Each morning, the teacher writes the vegetables and main dishes on the board, and students make selections as they enter the classroom. For example, suppose Vegetable 1 is corn, Vegetable 2 is green beans, Main dish 1 is chicken, and Main dish 2 is pizza. This means that Pam chose green beans and chicken, Tom chose corn and pizza, and Jose chose green beans and pizza.

Magnetic buttons with children's names or small photographs could

allow the children to create "instant" graphs that the class can then discuss. A permanent lunch-count graph could also serve as an attendance check. Each morning, label the columns with the lunch choices, including the choice of "lunch box." The children place their magnet in the appropriate place on the grid when they arrive in the morning.

When using buttons, magnets, or clothespins with children's names, let the children take turns putting names in alphabetical order at the end of the day so they will be ready to use the next morning.

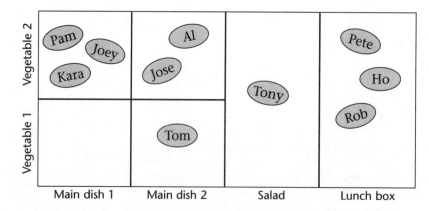

From the Classroom

Kitty McGimsey encouraged her class to help solve a problem for the cafeteria workers. Each week they recorded how many forks and spoons were lost from the lunchroom and displayed the data on a hall bulletin board. On the bulletin board, the students suggested some reasons for the losses (such as silverware being accidentally thrown in the trash or packed into lunch boxes) and asked other students for suggestions on how the school could solve the problem.

Judy Foster's grade 3 class constructed three-dimensional bar graphs about what they drank at lunch. They sorted their empty drink cartons by flavor and then arranged the cartons into bars to make a drink-carton bar graph.

Analyzing the Data

Give several children the opportunity to read the data from the displays they have created to show lunch choices. If any of the data displays are new or unusual representations, allow time for the children to explain. For example, the grid used by Tammy Cullom's class may need explanation if the children have never seen this type of matrix before.

Here are our choices for lunch today. Which did we order more of—[pizza] or [grilled cheese sandwiches]? How can we tell? The cooks want us to give them a piece of paper that will tell them what we want for lunch. Is everyone accounted for? Who would like to fill out our form?

Interpreting the Results

Why do you think we ordered more [pizza]? Do you think [pizza] would have been the most popular choice if [chicken] had been the other entree instead of [grilled cheese sandwiches]? How might we figure this out for sure? Which method do you think is best for collecting these data? Why? What's the best way to give this information to the cooks?

Simple investigations with the entire class can often be the starting point for more complex or divergent investigations by portions of the class. For example, some children may be interested in how the lunch order from their class compares with that of classes in other grades.

Do you think the [grade 3] class also ordered more [pizza] than [grilled cheese sandwiches]? How could we find out?

Other children may want to investigate what the most popular lunch choices are throughout the school. As an extension, you might encourage small groups or pairs of children to formulate specific questions related to school lunches, plan how they want to gather the data, and conduct their own investigations. The children can make a data display and present their findings to the class.

Teacher Note

Another way to create magnetic markers is to cut off the bottom of individual milk cartons, leaving a quarter-inch frame around the sides, and glue magnetic strips on the back of the cartons. The children color their pictures on small squares of paper, add their names, and glue them inside the milk-carton frames.

Extension

Challenge the children to design a better food tray. What spaces or compartments are needed? How big do they need to be? Should there be right-handed and left-handed trays?

Fun Facts

- Sandwiches were named after the Earl of Sandwich. He did not want to take time from playing card games to eat, so he asked his cook to place his meat between two pieces of bread so he could eat and play at the same time.
- Rice is the chief food for half the people of the world. There are 15,000 different kinds of rice.
- Potato chips were invented by an African-American chef in Louisiana in 1865.
- In the United States in 1976, a pound of potato chips cost 200 times more than a pound of potatoes. What is this ratio today?
- Cabbage is 91% water.
- Honey found in the tombs of Egyptian pharaohs has been found edible by archaeologists.

Extension

Consider having the children write or draw their own book about food. This might be a collection of interesting facts, favorite recipes, or data about the eating habits, such as whether or not students eat breakfast or what beverage they drink with dinner. *Smashed Potatoes: A Kid's-eye View of the Kitchen* is a fun collection of original recipes written by young children. This book includes several recipes for "Skabbetti" or "Basketti" with ingredients like "41 sausages as big as your ear."

Some children may be interested in recording which foods in the food pyramid they eat each day and collecting data over time to evaluate their eating habits.

To encourage the children to come up with their own investigations, ask more questions about their school lunches.

Do the seasons of the year relate to the amount of milk we drink at lunch? Do our choices of drink flavor relate to the entree we have?

Results of simple data gathering like this can be recorded on paper graphs and collected over time. Later in the year, the children can analyze and interpret changes—as in their choice of drink flavor—during the school year.

How Many of Each Pattern Block Should Be in a Set?

School activities often give rise to investigation questions. How many sheets of paper do we use? How do we keep score while playing this game? How many pairs of scissors do we need to borrow? Investigations designed to help answer such questions are relevant for children because of their direct experience with the topics.

An authentic problem for teachers is figuring out how many pattern blocks are needed for different activities in the classroom. When the children are creating their own designs, will there be enough of a given shape? Which blocks are the children most likely to use? Does this vary according to the activity?

During this three-part investigation, the children help answer some of these questions by exploring the statistics of their own work with pattern blocks. The investigation provides data about the most frequently used pattern blocks. The children can record the data by creating tables and charts with paper versions of the pattern blocks used in their designs, or by making graphs.

Before the children begin these activities, they should have had time to become familiar with pattern blocks by creating patterns, making large designs, and exploring the geometry of the blocks. They also need opportunities to discuss colors and shapes, to explore the relationships between the areas of the blocks—such as the fact that two trapezoids cover the area of one hexagon—and to compare the lengths of the sides of the different pattern blocks.

Activity A

Posing the Question

In this first activity, the children create their own designs and make graphs of the blocks they use. Ask questions to start them thinking about their use of pattern blocks.

Which pattern block do you think you use the most? Will the answer be the same for all students? Will it be the same for different activities? Will the blocks students use the most also be their favorite blocks? Is your favorite block the class's favorite block? How can we find out?

Connections

Art
- exploring and creating patterns
- creating symmetrical designs

Literature
- *Anno's Math Games III* by Misumasa Anno (New York: Philomel Books, 1991)
- *The Greedy Triangle* by Marilyn Burns (New York: Scholastic, 1994)

Extension

Have the children use the front of a folded sheet of colored construction paper to design a cover for their math journals. They can create the design with pattern blocks and make the cover by pasting on paper pattern blocks, stamping the pattern block design, or tracing and coloring the shapes.

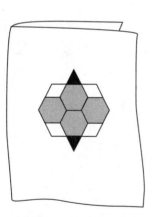

Collecting Data

Put the children into pairs, and distribute the pattern blocks and half sheets of paper.

Make a design or picture using pattern blocks that fits on your sheet of paper. When you finish your picture, tell your partner about it.

It may take some children a long time to experiment with their designs, which offers you an ideal opportunity for informal, individual assessment. While the children are engaged with the blocks, you can circulate and ask the children to identify colors and shapes, to model symmetry, or to show you ways to cover the hexagon with other combinations of blocks. It is also interesting to note which children build up rather than just creating flat designs.

We want to find out which pattern blocks we use the most. How could you show the different blocks you used in your design?

Rather than telling the children exactly how to display their results, allow them to devise a variety of approaches. If the children need ideas, you might suggest that they use their graphing mats, or that they group like blocks and count each group.

Young children might place their blocks on a graphing mat before making pictorial or more abstract representations. Individual graphing mats could be made by drawing grids on 12 inch by 18 inch construction paper or legal-size file folders. Then they can record the information by pasting paper pattern blocks or coloring squares on a paper graph, such as the "Pattern Block Record Sheet." Graphing mats or grid paper are useful, because only one block fits in each square on the grid, regardless of the block's size.

Experienced children might sort, count, and graph the number of each block. They may be able to design their own grids for recording the data. Seeing different types of data displays around the room will give the children more ideas and encourage them to explore other ways to organize their data.

From the Classroom

A grade 1 teacher asked her students to fold a piece of paper in half and cut out a heart. Students then sorted their hearts into three columns according to size: large, medium, and small. The big hearts made a taller column because of their larger size. The students focused upon the size of the column rather than the number of hearts and concluded that more students had cut out large hearts than the other two sizes. They had actually cut out more medium-size hearts, so the teacher decided to use graphing mats to help her students focus on number rather than size. Young students typically focus on size rather than number when making decisions about what is more. This may be a result of their not yet having constructed one-to-one correspondence or developed conservation of number.

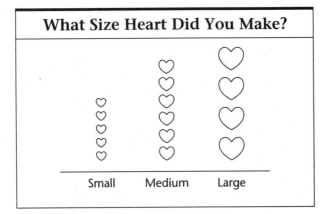

What Size Heart Did You Make?

Small   Medium   Large

Analyzing the Data

After the children make their individual graphs, talk about the results.

Which block did you use the most in your design? Did anyone else use that shape the most? What else can you say about your graph?

Look for children who used none of a particular shape, and ask them to talk about their graphs. If no child has a zero in their data, create your own design, omitting one shape, and share your results with the class.

What does it mean when there are no squares colored for a shape?

Share your graph with three other students. Notice how many of each block was used by each person.

Allow groups of four to explore this idea.

Teacher Note

You may need to create a sample with zero as a data point if no child does this.

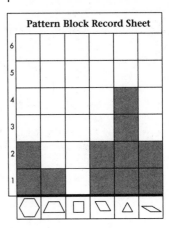

Pattern Block Record Sheet

Extension

Use pattern blocks to create borders for bulletin boards by creating patterns on adding-machine tape with templates or by using paper pattern blocks. Or, the children could trace around actual blocks and then color the shapes.

Teacher Note

As the children play, remind them to think about finding a winning strategy.
■ Does it matter if you go first or second?
■ Are there always the same number of blocks on the board when the game is finished?

How could we organize ourselves to find out how many other students used the same block the most?

Let the children suggest ways to group and display their graphs so that they are all visible at the same time.

What can we say about the pattern blocks that are used the most in our class? Guess how many blocks the entire class used in all the designs. How did you make your guess? Suppose we wanted to show all the blocks we used on one graph. How might we make this big graph?

You or the children can write sentence strips to post near the individual graphs or near the graph showing the combined data. Encourage the children to compare their individual graphs with the data on the class graph.

Interpreting the Results

Is the block you used the most in your design also your favorite block? Do you think you would be able to use your favorite block the most in every activity?

Do you think the people who sell pattern blocks put the best mix of blocks into a set? Would you change the mix of pattern blocks in a set? If so, how? Why? Suppose we had more hexagons in our classroom. Do you think our graphs would be different?

Most packaged building sets include a list of the number of each type of piece in the set, along with pictures of structures that could be built from the pieces. If possible, show such a building set and contents list to the children.

Why do you think the makers of toys like this set of building blocks put a list of the blocks in the package? Why do you think the list shows pictures of some of the things you can make with the set? How do you think the manufacturers decide how many of each piece or block to put in a package?

Activity B

Posing the Question

Nim games are simple pattern games for partners.

I have a game we can play with our pattern blocks. The game is called Kitty Nim. For this game, we will use only the trapezoids, hexagons, blue parallelograms (rhombuses), and triangles. After we play the game, we can talk again about how we might package sets of pattern blocks.

To play Kitty Nim, each pair of children needs a "Kitty Nim Game Board" and several of the four pattern blocks mentioned on page 20. The object is to cover the kitty's face with blocks. The person who places the last block on the game board, completing the design, wins the game.

Kitty Nim Game Board

Partners take turns placing any one of the available blocks on the game board. When a block is placed on the game board, at least one side of the block must line up with at least one line on the board.

Consider introducing the game by playing a sample game at the over-head projector. Before the children play, make sure everyone understands the rules about how to play.

While you play the game, think about these questions: Do you find that you use one block more often than the others? Is that because you like that block, or because you have a strategy to help you win?

Collecting the Data

At the end of each Kitty Nim game, you might have the children tally how many of each block they used. Tallying is a quick way to record the results of each game.

Since there are so many opportunities for children to recognize patterns in this game, you may decide to encourage them to play first with the goal of finding strategies for winning and later return to the questions about the blocks used most frequently and how many of each block were used.

You might have the children create a class chart to record the blocks they use in each game. After several days of play, volunteers could use their calculators to find the total for every kind of block.

Analyzing the Data

This activity will help the children to discover more about which blocks and how many of each block should be packaged for a variety of purposes. The children need to determine the maximum number of any one block needed to play the Kitty Nim game.

What have you noticed about how many of each block you used while playing Kitty Nim?

As the children report numbers from specific games, encourage them to look for relationships. For example, the number of larger blocks, such as the hexagon, required are generally smaller.

Kitty Nim Game Board

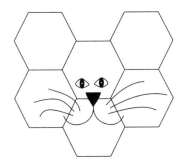

Sample Kitty Nim Game

Move 1
Player A
places trapezoid

Move 2
Player B
places hexagon

Move 3
Player A
places blue rhombus

Move 4
Player B
places triangle

Move 5
Player A
places hexagon

Move 6
Player B
places triangle

Play continues until a player places the last piece.

What is the greatest number of hexagons any pair used in a game? What is the fewest number of hexagons used in any game?

Continue this discussion by asking about each pattern block.

Remind the children that when the game was introduced, you had the children use only hexagons, trapezoids, blue rhombuses, and triangles.

Why were the squares and tan rhombuses not used? (They will not cover the game board without leaving open spaces. These two blocks could be considered zero points in the data.)

Interpreting the Results

The largest number of any one block actually used by the children in a game of Kitty Nim, may not be the same as the maximum possible number that could be placed on the game board. For example, six hexagons could be used to cover the "Kitty Nim Game Board," while it is possible that no pair recorded more than four hexagons used during a game. Since the children are playing to win, they may not have chosen to place only hexagons on the game board.

How might the data from our game results help us to decide how many of each block to package for Kitty Nim?

This might generate a discussion about how to use data in making decisions. Even though the maximum number of hexagons needed to cover the board is six, the children may decide that fewer hexagons would work as well and be more practical.

Have the children create game sets for Kitty Nim by packaging "Kitty Nim Game Boards" and the number of each block they recommend for playing the game. If possible, arrange for the children to visit another class to "field test" their packaging plan. Each student would pair with a student from the other class and teach that student the Kitty Nim game.

If you have time and the children are still interested, have them explore variations on the game, during choice activity time or at a center. Data could be collected gradually over time and then interpreted at a later date.

If we changed the rules for Kitty Nim so that the person placing the last piece loses, would this change our decision about the number of each block to package?

How might changing the shape of the game board affect our decision?

Suppose you had no green triangles. How would this change the numbers of the other blocks you would package?

Activity C

Posing the Question

In Activity A, the children found which pattern blocks they use most frequently when they are free to create any kind of design they wish. In Activity B, the choice of blocks was limited by the Kitty Nim game. In this activity, the children will look for all the possible ways to cover a given design.

Distribute a copy of the "Design It" sheet to each pair. (Allowing children to work with a partner requires fewer blocks and encourages them to work together to avoid duplications, yet still find all the possibilities.)

Today we are going to investigate all the ways we can cover a design with pattern blocks. Compare this design with the Kitty Nim game board. Do you think we will use a different set of blocks for this design? Do you think we will need different numbers of each block for this activity? Why might the blocks we use be different for different activities?

The children may notice that the tan rhombuses will fit on this design. Have them consider whether or not the squares will fit on this design.

Collecting the Data

Have the children work in pairs to fill in "Design It" Outline 1 in as many ways as they can and to record which blocks they use each time they fill in the outline. The recording strategies the children used for Activity B will work well for this activity.

One Way to Cover "Design It" Outline 1

Sample "Pattern Block Record Sheet"

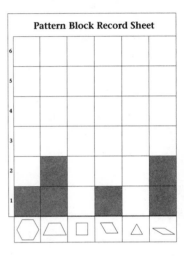

From the Classroom

Tammy Cullom found that making a chart to list all possibilities was a strategy many of her students used frequently once they had completed several activities like this one. Tammy moved with her students from grade 1 to grade 2. By the end of grade 2, almost every student was representing data in more than one way as a matter of choice. They answered numerous questions related to their likes and dislikes and even included family members and others in the school and community in their investigations.

Analyzing the Data

When the children feel sure they have found all the possible ways to cover Outline 1, have them focus on the data they have recorded with their partners.

How many different ways did you and your partner find to cover this outline? [Carla and Tomeka] say that there are six different ways, but [Ian and Harold] think there are seven. What do the rest of you think? How can you prove your idea? How can we be sure we have found all of the ways?

What is the fewest number of blocks a pair used? What is the greatest number of blocks used?

Can we use every number of blocks in between?

If the children do not suggest this, you might suggest reordering the information to create an organized approach to answering the last question. Write on the board the smallest number used and the greatest number used by any pair, leaving space to fill in the numbers between them. For example, one pair may have used 5 blocks and another pair 14 blocks. List 5 through 14, and ask whether any group used 6 blocks; put a check mark beside the number. Continue until the class has explored every number.

Remind the children that the questions they are trying to answer are which blocks are used, and how many of each block are used. When the design is covered with five blocks, which blocks and how many of each are used? This could be listed next to the number 5 on the board. For example, 5 = 2 hexagons + 2 tan rhombuses + 1 blue rhombus.

How can we use the information about all of the different ways to cover the design to answer our question about which blocks are used?

The children should notice that the square was not used, while all of the other blocks were.

How can we use this information to answer our question about how many of each block are used?

This question is more complex. The children may return to the strategy used for activity B by focusing on the maximum number of any kind of block used when covering the design. For example, the maximum number of yellow hexagons is two, which is possible when the design is covered with five or six blocks. You may want to divide the children into small groups to work with one or two specific kinds of blocks, such as hexagons and trapezoids.

Interpreting the Results

Do you think we would have similar results if we used a different outline?

Consider having half the class cover Outline 1 while the other half covers Outline 2. Have them compare the blocks they used and discuss possible reasons for any differences. Then, have the children create their own outlines.

Could you make an outline that would use more tan parallelograms than triangles?

Bring the class back together to return to the question of how to package sets of blocks.

We have done lots of activities with pattern blocks. We have discovered that we use different pattern blocks for different activities. If you manufactured pattern blocks, how would you decide how many of each block to put in a set?

After the discussion, ask the children to summarize their findings, and to add their own ideas in a letter to a company explaining how they would package the pattern blocks and why. The children may write individual letters or dictate a class letter. (Use educational supply catalogs to find company addresses.) Corresponding with companies can be very rewarding for students, especially when they receive a response.

Pattern Blocks: Yellow Hexagons

Pattern Blocks: Orange Squares

Pattern Blocks: Red Trapezoids

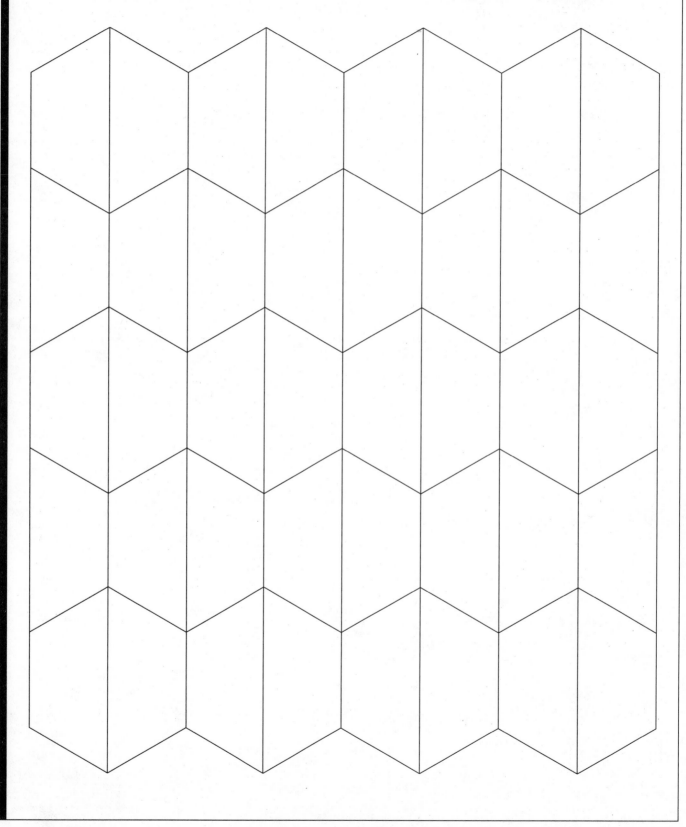

Pattern Blocks: Tan Parallelograms

Pattern Blocks: Green Triangles

Pattern Blocks: Blue Rhombuses

Pattern Block Record Sheet

6					
5					
4					
3					
2					
1					

Design It Outline 1

How many different ways can you cover this design?

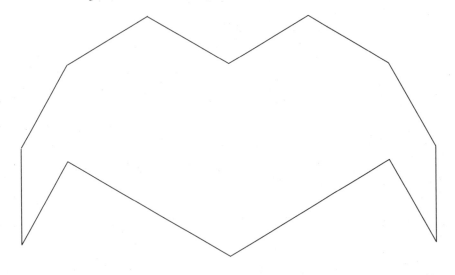

Design It Outline 2

How many different ways can you cover this design?

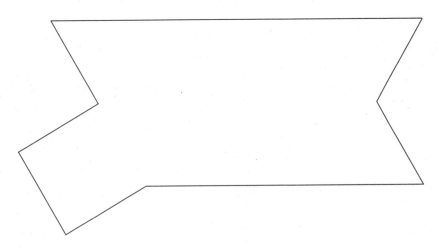

Kitty Nim Game Board

Rules

1. Use hexagons, trapezoids, blue parallelograms, and triangles.

2. Take turns putting a block on the board.

3. You win by placing the last block on the board.

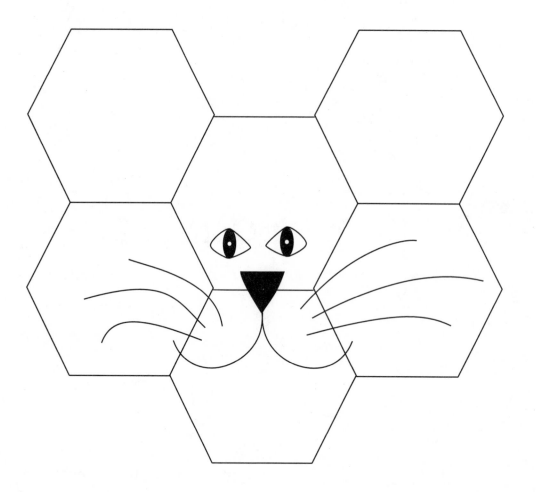

How Many Seeds Are in a Pumpkin?

- making and revising estimates
- counting and ordering large numbers
- grouping hundreds, tens, and ones
- finding range, median, and mode *(optional)*
- graphing the same data using different scales *(optional)*

Materials

- 1 medium-size pumpkin
- stick-on notes *(1 per child)*
- chart paper *(optional)*
- knife, large spoon, and paper towels
- strips of green construction paper *(long enough for 10 pumpkin seeds—about 4")*
- rectangles of brown construction paper *(large enough for 10 green strips—about 5" by 11")*
- large pumpkin cut from orange construction paper
- glue
- "Pumpkin Seed Data" sheet *(optional; 1 per pair)*

Connections

Social Studies
- studying Native Americans and colonists

Science
- growing plants

Literature
- *The Vanishing Pumpkin* by Tony Johnston (New York: Putnam, 1990)
- *The Pumpkin Patch* by Elizabeth King (New York: Dutton, 1990)
- *The Biggest Pumpkin Ever* by Steven Kroll (New York: Scholastic, 1985)
- *Pumpkin, Pumpkin* by Jeanne Titherington (New York: Greenwillow, 1986)

Mathematics in the primary grades is not a series of discrete, unrelated lessons. Many lessons, such as this one, include the overall goal of helping children to develop an understanding of our place-value system while focusing on other mathematical content or skills.

This is a two-part investigation. Younger children may complete only the first activity, while older children could complete both parts.

In Activity A, the whole class first explores questions about a single pumpkin. The children guess the number of seeds in the pumpkin, then look inside the pumpkin and make new estimates. Finally, they count the seeds and then display them by ones, tens, and hundreds.

In Activity B, pairs of children work with previously collected data to make predictions about the number of seeds in other pumpkins. If several classes complete the activities, the children will have opportunities to compare their predictions to actual results. Even small pumpkins often contain hundreds of seeds. Graphing the number of seeds in pumpkins provides children with opportunities for working with large amounts of data and wide ranges. The children may graph their data several times, using different intervals and comparing the shapes of the displays.

Activity A

Posing the Question

Hold up your pumpkin.

Is this a small pumpkin or a large pumpkin? How many seeds do you think are in this pumpkin? Why? Have you ever counted the seeds in a pumpkin?

Ask the children to each write a guess of the number of seeds on a stick-on note. Draw a line across the bottom of the board or a piece of chart paper, and write a 0 at the left end of the line.

Who thinks they might have the smallest guess? [Sharonda] says her guess is [20]. Did anyone guess less than that? Who thinks they have the largest guess? [Luke] says he guessed [800]. Is there a higher guess?

As the children share their guesses, determine the lowest and highest guesses and write these on the line.

These two numbers—the lowest guess and the highest guess—are the range of our guesses.

Now I am going to give you a little information so you can change your guess if you want to. I am going to cut the top off my pumpkin and let you look inside.

Cut the pumpkin open, and allow the children to look inside and change their numbers if they want to. At this point, the children are making estimates, not just guesses. An estimate is a guess based on some kind of experience or information.

Help the children place their stick-on notes above the line from least to greatest. It may be helpful to write additional numbers between the smallest and largest estimates to serve as benchmarks. The children may also need help placing their stick-on notes in columns when estimates are duplicated. The intervals between numbers do not need to be equal; the important thing is the order.

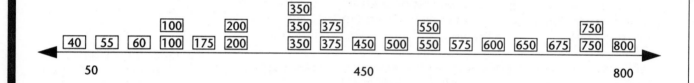

What is the range now? Has it changed? Why?

Collecting the Data

Now we are going to count the seeds in this pumpkin.

Put the children into small groups. Empty the pumpkin, and give a cluster of seeds to each group.

Count the number of seeds that I give you. You may want to make piles of 10 seeds to make counting easier.

Next, give groups strips of green paper.

Glue a column of 10 seeds on each strip of paper. Work with another group or groups to combine your leftover seeds into groups of 10.

As a class, count all the seeds by tens to determine the number of seeds in the pumpkin. There will probably be over 100 seeds. If so, have the children create groups of 100 seeds by gluing 10 green strips to a brown rectangle. Then, they can glue all of the seeds to a large orange paper pumpkin in groups of hundreds, tens, and leftover ones.

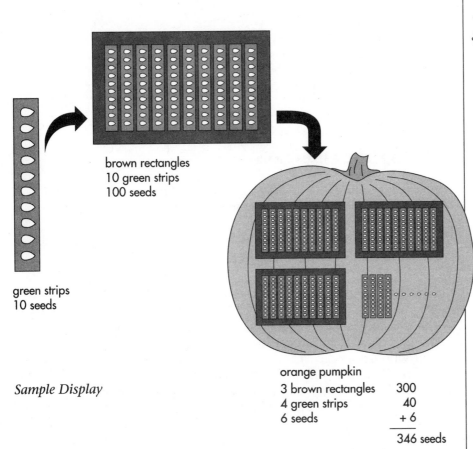

green strips
10 seeds

brown rectangles
10 green strips
100 seeds

Sample Display

orange pumpkin

3 brown rectangles	300
4 green strips	40
6 seeds	+ 6
	346 seeds

Analyzing the Data

How many seeds were in our pumpkin? How does our display help us know how many seeds were in it? Were you surprised by the number of seeds in our pumpkin? How do our estimates compare with the actual number of seeds?

The children will probably first compare their personal estimates with the total.

Can we say anything about how well we estimated as a group?

Help the children compare the total number of seeds with the estimate made most often, which is the mode. You might also want to compare this number with the middle estimate, which is the median. Discuss the range as well. While the actual seed count is not represented with a traditional data display, the children's estimates were represented with a line plot, which is a traditional data representation.

Interpreting the Results

Do you think other pumpkins have the same number of seeds that ours had? Is the size of a pumpkin related to the number of seeds it contains?

Extension

The children might be inspired by this activity to grow pumpkins, to visit a commercial pumpkin farm, or to collect pumpkin recipes, poems, and stories. They might also want to research the nutritional value of pumpkins and squash, or how gourds are used to make musical instruments.

Discuss the need for more information, which could be gathered by looking at a larger sample.

Does this one example tell us about all pumpkins?

Activity B

Posing the Question

How many seeds did we count in our pumpkin? If we open another pumpkin, how many seeds do you think we will find?

The children are likely to assume that the size of a pumpkin is related to the number of seeds it contains.

Collecting the Data

The data for this investigation can come from several sources. The children may want to open their own pumpkins. Other classes in your school may have investigated pumpkin-seed counts and have data to share. Or, you can use the data from the "Pumpkin Seed Data" sheet, which is actual data that was collected by a real class. If you choose to use these data, distribute a copy of "Pumpkin Seed Data" to each pair.

Here is a list showing the number of seeds counted by another class of students. All of their pumpkins were about the same size. What can you say about these pumpkins by just looking at the chart?

The children may notice that there are more than 300 seeds in every pumpkin, or that none of the pumpkins has as many as 600 seeds.

Analyzing the Data

Have the children organize and plan displays of the data. They might choose, for example, to list all the seeds from pumpkins with 300–399 seeds on one pumpkin shape, those with 400–499 seeds on another pumpkin shape, and those with 500–599 on a third. Or they might want to make a chart listing their seed counts from least to greatest.

Before the children create their displays, discuss the important parts of a display, including a title and appropriate labels.

How have you organized the data? Did anyone arrange the numbers from lowest to highest? What do you need to decide about how to display this data collection?

This activity provides an opportunity for you to help the children explore how different scales may be used to graph the same data. The children may decide to create several graphs of the data, giving each graph a different scale. Graphing the same data with different scales will help the children see how the same information can look very different. Manipulating the scale on a graph is a strategy often used to persuade people to think a certain way.

Interpreting the Results

Help the children interpret their data displays.

What do our investigations tell us about the number of seeds in a pumpkin of about the same size? What can we say about the range of our data—the pumpkins with the most seeds and those with the least seeds?

If we were to open another pumpkin, about how many seeds do you think we would find?

You might ask the children to write their ideas in their math journals and explain their thinking.

Teacher Note

Range A measure of spread or variation stated in terms of the lowest and the highest values in a data set.
Mode The value that occurs most often in a data set.
Median The value that is the middle of an ordered set of data.

From the Classroom

Lorraine J. Malphurs' grade 2 class began a pumpkin investigation by reading aloud the book *Pumpkin, Pumpkin.* Several other classes at her school also investigated pumpkins. Each class displayed its seed counts for the other classes to use as data. The classes glued the seeds onto a large orange paper pumpkin that hung in the hallway. Groups of 10 seeds were glued to a strip of green paper, groups of 10 strips were glued to a brown rectangle, and brown rectangles—along with any remaining strips of green tens and single seeds—were glued to the paper pumpkin. Their display reinforced place value by grouping seeds by hundreds, tens, and ones.

Lisa Williamson had her students compare the number of seeds in different kinds of pumpkins and squashes. The gourd family—which includes pumpkins, squashes, cucumbers, and melons—produces fruit that is varied in size, shape, color, texture, and taste. Many can be found in today's supermarkets and offer wonderful opportunities for investigations about seeds.

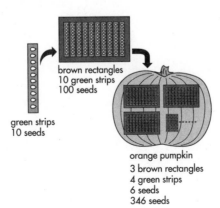

brown rectangles
10 green strips
100 seeds

green strips
10 seeds

orange pumpkin
3 brown rectangles
4 green strips
6 seeds
346 seeds

Teacher to Teacher

Labeling Data Displays

Labeling a data display appropriately is critical to making it understandable. Children need consistent reminders to label all parts of their graphs and displays, as they tend to omit such details.

- **Title** Every data display needs a title. Titles should communicate as much as possible about the subject using as few words as possible. A first step in labeling displays might be to write the question posed. For example, "How Many Seeds Are in a Pumpkin?"

- **Scale** Information and labels about scale will vary greatly depending upon the type of graph.

- **Key** Pictographs must have a key providing information about the value of each picture used in the graph. For example, one picture of a pumpkin might stand for 10 seeds.

- **Axis labels** In a bar graph, each axis needs a label. For example, a bar graph showing what kind of face children carved on their pumpkins might have a bar for each kind of face: happy, sad, and scary. The length of each bar indicates the number of children carving that expression and is indicated by numbers on the axis.

Children may also need encouragement to create displays that are neat, inviting, and easy to read.

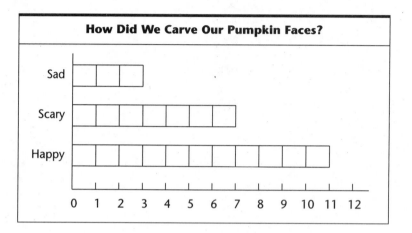

Pumpkin Seed Data

Student	Number of seeds
Thomas	381
Andy	325
Pierina	365
Olivia	410
Ginny	467
Kate	479
Mathieu	512
Geoffrey	494
Zachary	455
Beth	367
Rachel	507
James	384
Elizabeth	545
Kristin	568
Lindsay	408

These data were supplied by
Lorraine J. Malphurs' grade 2 class.

How Do We Eat Gingerbread Cookies?

Mathematical Focus

- sorting, grouping, and counting
- collecting, organizing, and describing data
- creating a bar graph

This investigation capitalizes on children's natural interest in food and eating. After hearing or reading a story about gingerbread people, the children are given gingerbread cookies and asked to take just one bite. The parts of the cookies removed with their first bites become the data. The children then tear off the part that they bit from a paper model of a gingerbread cookie and use the paper cookies to make graphs of their first bites. (Before conducting this activity, please check that none of the children is diabetic or has allergies or other dietary concerns, and adjust the activity accordingly.)

Materials

- napkins
- gingerbread people cookies (*1 per child*)
- "Paper Cookies" (*1 cookie per child*)
- paper squares to accommodate the "Paper Cookies" (*optional*)
- large chart paper or grid
- glue
- animal crackers (*optional*)
- Teddy Grahams graham snacks (*optional*)
- "Teddy Grahams Sorting Mat" (*optional; 1 per child*)

Posing the Question

Generating discussion and making predictions is an important aspect of investigating data. However, it is also important that such discussions not influence outcomes. If the children discuss which part of a gingerbread person they think most of them will bite off first, this could influence their first bites. To prevent such bias, you might ask the children to think about a question without expressing their thoughts aloud.

Think about how you would answer the following question, but don't say your answer aloud: When we are eating our gingerbread people, what part do we bite off first?

Connections

Measurement
- cooking and measuring capacities

Literature
- sequencing events
- writing predictable stories (*optional*)
- *The Gingerbread Guide: Using Folktales with Young Children* by Linda Garrity (Glenview, Illinois: GoodYear Books, 1987)
- *The Gingerbread Man* by Eric A. Kimmel (New York: Holiday House, 1993)

Collecting the Data

Distribute napkins and gingerbread cookies.

When you get your cookie, please take just one bite. You will be able to eat the rest very soon.

Next, distribute one of the "Paper Cookies" to each child.

Tear off the part that matches the bite you took from the real cookie. Now, you can enjoy what is left of your cookie!

Analyzing the Data

Lead a discussion about the results.

How many of you bit off the head first? How about a leg? How about an arm? Are there other categories? For example, are some cookies missing half a body or both legs?

What is the best way to show our results?

The children may suggest putting all of their "Paper Cookies" together according to what part is missing. For example, all the "Paper Cookies" with heads missing could be glued to a larger piece of paper cut in the shape of a gingerbread person. Or, the children may suggest making some kind of bar graph.

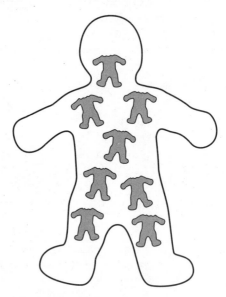

If we make a bar graph, how will we make sure each "Paper Cookie" takes up the same amount of space on our graph?

In this discussion, you want the children to focus on where they took their first bite, not on the size of the cookie that remained.

Based on their prior experience with this issue, the children may suggest gluing their "Paper Cookies" to a square first and then making the bar graph, or gluing them onto a large grid.

Interpreting the Results

What can we say about how we eat gingerbread cookies? Which part did the largest number of students eat first? Why do you think this is? If we did this investigation with another class, do you think the results would be the same?

What other questions might we ask about how we eat things?

Teacher Note

How people go about eating a particular food is sometimes related to cultural traditions. For example, in Japan it is considered impolite to bite into an apple. The only proper way to eat an apple in Japan is to slice it with a knife and eat the slices.

From the Classroom

Debbie Hill used the theme from the classic story about the gingerbread man to familiarize her students with the school during the first few days of class. After reading the story, she told her students that the gingerbread man had been spotted in the principal's office—and that they were all going to catch him! She walked her students to the principal's office and introduced them to the principal and secretaries. The principal, who was in on the plan, said the gingerbread man had run off to the lunchroom. The class walked to the lunchroom, where they met the food-service staff. One of the cooks said the gingerbread man had run off to the library. This continued until students had visited much of the school and its staff. At the last location, students were told that the gingerbread man had last been seen running to their classroom. Upon returning to class, students found a whole tray of gingerbread cookies just waiting to be eaten.

You may want to substitute or use variations of this investigation to expand the children's experiences with this activity. Young children need many opportunities to revisit concepts in order to construct their understanding.

In one variation, you can have the children investigate how they eat animal crackers. Because animal crackers are smaller, ask the children to take very small bites. They can then draw and cut out paper animal crackers and tear off the part corresponding to their first bite.

Teddy Grahams® graham snacks provide material for several investigations because they come in three flavors and with their hands up or down. You could give the children one, or more, of each flavor to taste.

What is your favorite flavor? Do you think more of us prefer chocolate, cinnamon, or honey?

The children might indicate their favorite flavor by coloring a paper bear brown for chocolate, red for cinnamon, and orange for honey; let the children decide on the colors as a group.

If I give you a handful of these graham crackers, do you think you will have more with their hands up or their hands down? Or, do you think the numbers will be about the same?

Give each child a napkin and a handful of Teddy Grahams.

Sort and count your crackers to find out how many have their hands up and how many have their hands down.

The children may sort their cookies onto a "Teddy Graham Graphing Mat" or onto two napkins. Or, you might choose to have them place their handful of cookies on a personal graphing mat that they design (see "How to Make Graphing Mats" on p. 5).

Fun Facts

Gingerbread is the most ancient of sweet treats. It was discovered by a baker on the island of Rhodes about 2400 B.C. Many things, like gingerbread, that were invented by the Greeks were eventually copied by the Romans and spread throughout their vast empire. During the Dark Ages, directions for making gingerbread were preserved in monasteries. By the thirteenth century, ginger and gingerbread were well known in England. Queen Elizabeth I knew that her guests were fond of gingerbread, especially if the cake was molded in the image of the guest to whom it was offered. This practice proved so popular that she hired a special artist-baker whose sole task was to create gingerbread lords and ladies to amuse the courtiers. These were probably the first gingerbread people.

Teacher Note

If cooking is part of your school program, have the children make gingerbread or gingerbread cookies. This will provide opportunities for measuring dry and liquid ingredients. The children might even design and create gingerbread houses. Here's a recipe for edible "glue."

Architectural Icing
3 egg whites
½ teaspoon cream of tartar
1 box powdered sugar, sifted

Mix all the ingredients in a bowl using an electric mixer on low speed. Beat on high speed for 5 to 8 minutes until peaks form. Use grease-free utensils, and keep the mixture covered with a damp cloth while it is in use.

The rectangles in the mat would need to be 1" wide and 1¼" tall to accommodate the cookies. After the children have recorded their data, allow them to eat their cookies.

You may want to involve the children in planning a method for combining their data.

How many of you had more hands up? How many of you had more hands down? How many had the same number of hands up as hands down?

For older children, talk about combining their data into a total class picture. Ask them to think about whether or not the class graph will show the same results as their individual graphs. Ask the children to write about the activity either on the "Teddy Graham Graphing Mat" or in their math journals.

Paper Cookies

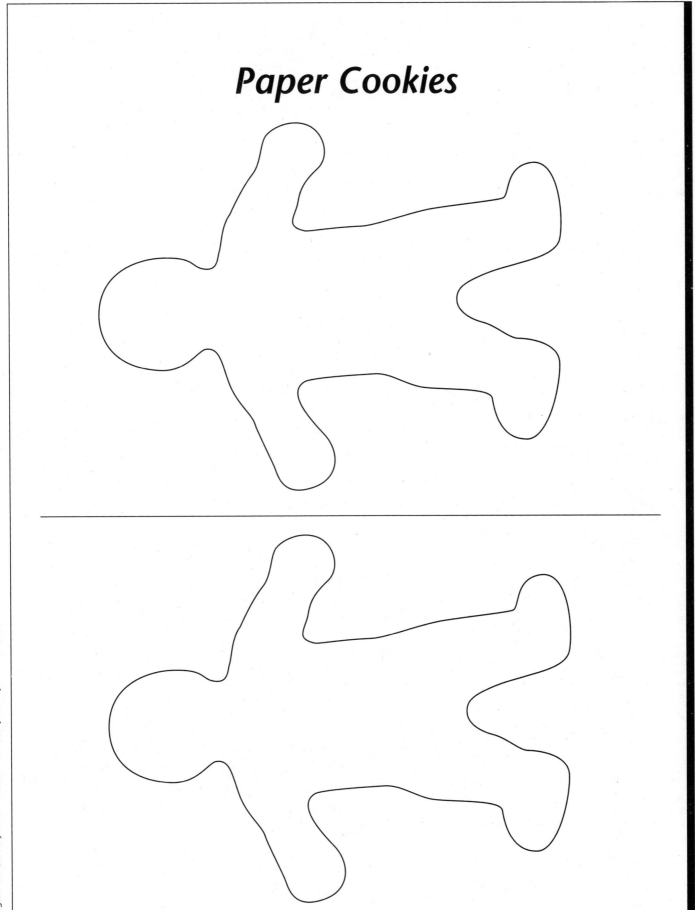

Teddy Grahams® Sorting Mat

Hands up	**Hands down**

When I counted the crackers in my handful,
I found . . .

_____

_____

_____

_____

_____

_____

_____

When we talked as a group, I learned . . .

_____

_____

_____

_____

_____

_____

_____

How Do We Like Our Eggs?

Mathematical Focus

- sorting and skip counting
- grouping
- collecting, organizing, and describing data
- creating a picture graph (pictograph)
- representing fractional parts

Materials

- small stick-on notes *(1 per child plus extras for interviews)*
- "Ways to Eat Eggs" sheets *(optional)*
- chart paper
- scissors *(optional)*

Connections

Science
- life science, studying oviparous animals

Communication Skills
- studying idioms
- writing

Literature
- *Chickens Aren't the Only Ones* by Ruth Heller (New York: Grosset and Dunlap, 1981)
- *Chicken Little* by Steven Kellogg (New York: Mullberry Books, 1985)
- *Chicka Chicka Boom Boom* by Bill Martin Jr. (New York: Simon and Schuster, 1989)

This activity offers another opportunity to capitalize upon children's interest in eating and food. Because of the richness of this topic, many extension ideas are included.

After collecting the data for this investigation, the children create a picture graph (or pictograph) using stick-on notes and paper eggs.

Posing the Question

When posing a question for investigation, always consider issues related to inclusion. Can everyone participate? Is everyone comfortable answering the question? We can't always predict how children or their families will react to a question posed for investigation, but it does help to consider these issues before proceeding. In this activity, children who do not eat eggs can participate by choosing "yuck" or something similar as their response.

How do you like your eggs? Is there anyone who does not eat or does not like eggs? Can we use "yuck" as a response for these students?

Write the responses on the board.

Collecting the Data

Direct the children's attention to the list they have generated about how they like their eggs. The children will need to learn how to phrase their questions so that, as they continue to survey others about preferences, people being surveyed are offered a limited number of choices. General questions such as "What is your favorite way to eat eggs?" can result in 26 different answers from 26 people. If necessary, help them limit their list to five or six choices.

For us to analyze and interpret our data, we need to limit the choices. Is there some way to group our choices so that we have only five or six?

The final list of choices might be scrambled, boiled, fried, deviled, and yuck. (Choices such as egg salad, coddled, and poached might be included with deviled or boiled.)

Teacher Note

Scientists group and classify animals according to a variety of attributes. One is whether or not an animal lays eggs. *Chickens Aren't the Only Ones* introduces children to the vast variety of animals classified as *oviparous,* or egg layers. Reading this book aloud would be a good way to launch this investigation. Children love to learn new and impressive words, and you can capitalize on their interest.

Extension

In *Chicken Little,* Steven Kellogg retells the classic story with a very funny twist. Foxy Loxy disguises himself as a policeman and drives around in his poultry wagon rounding up all the poultry. He's planning a poultry feast, but things don't quite work out according to plan. Consider reading an original version of *Chicken Little* and then Kellogg's version. Also consider retelling other classic "egg" or "bird" stories, such as *Jack and the Bean Stalk* and *The Ugly Duckling.* Ask the children what other favorite fairy tales they might like retold, and give them an opportunity to retell or rewrite some of them.

Label pieces of chart paper with the final choices. Labels might include pictures for children who are nonreaders. Distribute a stick-on note to each child, and ask each to write his or her name on the note and to post it on the appropriate chart.

If we wanted to know more about how people like their eggs, who else might we ask? Could we go home and ask our families how they like their eggs? Could we ask other people around our school? Could we interview students in another class?

Help the children create a plan for gathering more data in order to create a larger collection. They need to decide who to ask and how to keep track of the information they gather. They may decide to write names and preferences on stick-on notes, and add them to the charts when they return to class.

Analyzing the Data

If you plan to have the children compare their preferences with those of the people they interview outside the classroom, you may want to use different color stick-on notes for outsiders' data. Help the children organize their data so that their preferences are grouped together. Information from interviews can be organized separately. The children may want to create two different bar graphs.

Which is the most popular choice for eating eggs? Was scrambled eggs a popular choice for our class? Was it a popular choice for people not in our class? Is there any way to serve eggs that people do not seem to like at all?

How do our choices compare with those of the people we interviewed?

Depending upon the age of the children, you may wish to combine the data from the classroom with that of the people who were interviewed.

Let's put all of our data together. If we put all of the stick-on notes for scrambled eggs together, and do the same with all of the other choices, what will this tell us about the way people prefer to eat their eggs?

This provides a good opportunity for teaching children about picture graphs. In a picture graph, or pictograph, one picture represents more than one piece of information.

It might be easier to read our data if we combine our stick-on notes and create a picture graph. In a picture graph, one picture stands for more than one bit of information. For example, I might use a picture of a boiled egg to stand for these four stick-on notes.

A ratio of one paper egg to four stick-on notes may or may not be appropriate for your data and the children. The advantage of using one to four is that dividing a picture of a way to serve eggs into four pieces to show one, two, or three people is relatively easy. On the other hand, it might be easier for the children to count by fives. Use your own judgment when establishing this ratio.

You might want the class to use the pictures on the "Ways to Eat Eggs" sheet. The children could work in pairs to cut out pictures, drawing their own pictures for other ways to eat eggs if needed.

If we decide that one picture of scrambled eggs represents four stick-on notes, how many pictures of scrambled eggs will we need? Let's figure out how many pictures of the other kinds of eggs we will need.

Help the children organize the stick-on notes into groups of four (or whatever ratio you have established) on the paper eggs. This process will help them to understand that each egg stands for a certain number of people. When there are leftover stick-on notes, help the children decide what part of an egg is needed to accommodate them.

If we have two extra stick-on notes, how can we show this? What about one extra stick-on note? What about three extra stick-on notes?

Finally, help the children arrange the eggs into columns or rows on a piece of chart paper. Remind them to add labels to the chart, including a title and a key that gives the ratio of people to eggs.

Interpreting the Results

Bring the class back together to look at the displays of ways to eat eggs.

As we have been making our data displays, we have talked about how people like to eat their eggs. Who might be interested in knowing the results of our survey? Why might our information be important to a restaurant manager or a hospital dietitian?

How We Like Our Eggs

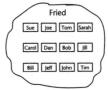

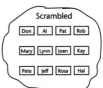

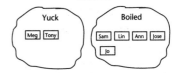

Picture Graph

Fun Facts

The largest eggs are laid by the ostrich, while the smallest are laid by the hummingbird.

From the Classroom

One teacher found that her students really enjoyed gathering data about their food preferences. In one of their investigations—"How Do We Like Our Potatoes?"—they settled on the following choices: French fried, baked, mashed, sweet, and French-fried sweet. They gathered their data through taste tests and surveyed two classes in addition to their own. Their enthusiasm spilled over into a full blown "tator" unit. The class decided to collect words containing -tator, such as agitator, initiator, imitator, dictator, spectator, and facilitator. They made "tator" people by stuffing brown paper bags and decorating them to create characters.

"Dick Tater"

"Spec Tater"

"Imi Tater"

Extension

Invite a chicken or poultry farmer to class to share information about chickens, such as the great variety of chickens or how many eggs a hen lays per day. Your local agricultural extension service or 4-H organization might have guest speakers available to visit schools. The children could brainstorm a list of questions to ask prior to the visit.

You might want to develop an entire egg unit based upon this beginning investigation. The children could collect egg recipes. One favorite for young children is "egg in the hole" (sometimes called "toad in the hole"). A hole is torn in the middle of a piece of bread, and the bread is fried in butter along with an egg that is dropped into the hole. The children could also collect sayings related to eggs and chickens—*scarce as hens' teeth, walking on eggs, henpecked, pecking order, chickenhearted*—and write a book with these expressions, explaining what each means. Or, how about collecting -egg words, like *eggsamine, eggscuse, eggsellent,* or *eggsercise?*

Ways to Eat Eggs

Scrambled

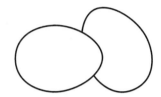

Hard Boiled

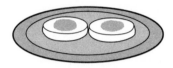

Poached

Egg Salad

Fried

Sunny Side Up

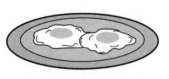

Over Easy

Yuck

How Big Are Our Shoe Prints?

Mathematical Focus

- sorting and classifying
- comparing and ordering
- counting and grouping
- finding the area of an irregular shape
- collecting, organizing, and describing data
- creating a line plot

Materials

- plain paper and peeled crayons *(1 per pair)*
- "Mystery Shoe Print" *(optional, 1 per pair)*
- grid paper *(1 sheet per child; see pp. 109–111)*
- chart paper *(optional)*
- stick-on notes *(1 per child)*

Connections

Literature
- *Peter and the Talking Shoes* by Katherine Banks (New York: Random House, 1994)
- *How Big Is a Foot?* by Rolf Myller (Bloomfield, Connecticut: Atheneum, 1962)
- *Shoes* by Elizabeth Winthrop (New York: Harper and Row, 1986)

One of the ways children notice their own growth is by their seemingly continual need for bigger and better shoes. This investigation capitalizes on children's natural interest in shoes and shoe size.

For this investigation, shoe size is determined by the number of square units in a shoe print outlined on grid paper. After investigating shoe prints in general, the children trace their shoes on grid paper and count the number of squares inside the outline. They create a line plot of their findings. From the line plot, the children could analyze the range of their data (the difference between the smallest data point and the greatest data point), the median (the midpoint of the data), and the mode or modes (the most popular data point or points).

Posing the Question

A great way to begin this investigation is by reading the book *Shoes*.

What is the difference between a footprint and a shoe print? Who might want to collect footprints? Why? Who might collect shoe prints? Why?

Discuss how anthropologists and trackers study animal prints to identify animals. You might want to talk about the legend of Big Foot or how criminologists use shoe prints to investigate crime scenes.

Patterns on the soles of today's shoes are extremely varied and interesting. Have the children work with a partner to make crayon rubbings of their shoe soles. They place a piece of paper over the sole of their partner's shoe and rub with a peeled crayon. The rubbings can be cut out and then sorted and grouped by different attributes.

How big is a shoe print? One way we might think about this question is to trace our shoe prints on grid paper. Then, we could count the number of squares inside the outline. Let's practice on this mystery shoe print.

Distribute copies of a shoe print—your own, someone else's, or the "Mystery Shoe Print"—traced on grid paper.

How might we count the number of squares inside this shoe print? How might we count the partial squares?

The children may suggest counting every other partial square or only those that are "mostly" inside the shoe print. Have pairs count the

Teacher Notes

You might choose to divide this investigation into shorter lessons for three consecutive days.

The "Mystery Shoe Print" is a child's shoe size 2. The print is traced on a one-inch grid and contains an area of approximately 17 square inches. It's important to connect this investigation of shoe size to measurement of area.

squares, using various approaches for counting partial squares, and then compare their results. Lead a discussion about how counting partial squares is not exact.

What do you think the smallest count will be? What do think the largest count will be? The range is the difference between the largest count and the smallest count. What kind of range do you expect with our counts of this shoe print?

How big are our shoe prints? How can we go about finding out? Is it important for all of us to wear a similar kind of shoe?

Facilitate this discussion until a clear plan emerges. Depending upon your schedule, this may end the first day of this investigation.

From the Classroom

Lynn Clark immediately engaged a class of grade 2 and 3 students by displaying her "Mystery Shoe Print" on the overhead projector and telling the students that some mystery person had faxed it to her the previous night. She wondered aloud who it might fit. (She used her own size 8½ shoe print.)

Working in pairs, her students began by cutting out copies of the mystery print and pasting it onto notebook paper. Each partner wrote a description of how they counted the square inches. One grade 3 pair colored the whole square inches as they were counted, and then paired up partial squares by labeling them with matching letters, such as A–A and B–B. One grade 3 student decided to trace partial squares onto a sheet of paper and move it around on top of the footprint until it combined with

another partial square to make a whole unit. She created a symbol to write in each matching partial square. The grade 2 students struggled with counting partial squares. This probably accounts for the spread in counts of the class—from 17 to 27½ square inches!

When students proceeded to gather their own data, some interesting questions were asked. Some students had a partner trace their shoe print while standing on the paper; others removed their shoe and did the tracing themselves. Students wondered whether this made a difference in the size of the resulting shoe print.

After creating their line plot, students found a median of 22 square inches, which matched the measure of three students' shoe prints. One student asked if these three people

all had the same length shoe. After checking, they found all three of the shoe lengths were different. One student explained that this made sense to her because someone could have a long, narrow foot while someone else could have a short, wide foot. This led to a discussion about shoe perimeter and whether similar-size prints had equal perimeters. Upon investigation, the perimeters of the three students' shoe prints were all different.

When returning to the mystery print, someone suggested that it belonged to someone in the room. It turned out that one boy's print did match the mystery print fairly well. Lynn asked him if he wore an 8½, as she knew the print was a women's 8½. His shoe size was a boy's 4½, which led to an interesting discussion about shoe sizes.

Collecting the Data

Help the children review their plan for collecting data to help answer the question, How big is a shoe print? One plan is for the children to work in pairs to trace each other's shoe on grid paper. Each child can then count the number of squares in his or her print and record the number on the paper. It might be helpful to have partners check each other's counts.

How will we count partial squares?

Even though counting partial squares is inexact, some kind of consistent approach is worth considering.

Have the children carry out their plan. Depending upon your schedule, you might decide to conclude for the day at this point and continue the next day.

Analyzing the Data

Help the children order their shoe prints from smallest to largest in a row across the floor. This will provide a concrete reference for the line plot the children are about to create. Another approach to this sorting and ordering is to have them arrange *themselves* in a line, by the size of their shoe print.

Ask the children to write the number of squares in their shoe print on a stick-on note. Draw a horizontal line on the board or on a piece of chart paper. By this time, the children should be aware of the smallest and largest shoe prints.

What is the smallest shoe print?

Write that number at the left end of the line, and write the number that is one less to the left of it.

What is the largest shoe print?

Write this number at the right end of the line, and write the number that is one greater to its right. Write a few of the numbers in between as benchmarks to help the children as they organize their stick-on notes along the line plot.

Help the children place their stick-on notes in the appropriate place along the axis. When two or more instances of a number occur, show the children how to place their notes in a vertical column over that number.

Extension

One teacher took her class outside to the playground area covered with sand. She had asked the custodian to wet the sand earlier in the day. Students had a great time making shoe prints in the wet sand. They even hid their eyes while the teacher chose one student to make several prints. Then, everyone tried to guess who made the prints.

Extension

Mystery Festival (1994; available from GEMS, Lawrence Hall of Science, University of California, Berkeley, California 94720) contains a mystery called "Who Borrowed Mr. Bear?" The assorted mysterious clues include shoe prints. Blackline masters and information are provided so the teacher can set the scene for the investigation of the mystery.

Fun Facts

- The first shoes were probably baglike wrappings made of animal skins. The ancient Egyptians wore sandals made from plant fiber or leather as early as 3700 B.C. In 1882, Jan Ernst Matzeliger, a Massachusetts shoe-factory worker, invented a "shoe-lasting" machine, which led to mass production of shoes by 1900. Today, shoes are designed on computer-controlled machine.
- The United States produced about 265 million pairs of shoes in 1993; 8 million were exported. Americans buy 845 million pairs of shoes a year imported from Brazil, Italy, Taiwan, and other countries. This accounts for 80% of the United States market for shoes. Do you know where the shoes you are wearing were manufactured? How might you find out?

Interpreting the Results

What can we say about our shoe prints?

This discussion will provide you with an opportunity to model the appropriate use of the terms *range, line plot, mode,* and *median.* You will need to decide which of these terms to use according to the children's experience.

What is the span between our smallest and largest shoe print? This is the range of our data. On this line plot, which column is the tallest? This is the mode, because it occurs most often.

If your line plot does not have a mode, or modes, you might add a few stick-on notes to one column and make up a story about some mystery shoe prints found in the class.

Which data piece is right in the middle? This is the median.

In order to have one data piece in the middle, there must be an odd number of shoe prints. If there is an even number of shoe prints, the median is midway between the two numbers.

Notice that we did not begin our line plot with the number 1. When you make a line plot, the numbers across the bottom can begin with the lowest data point instead of beginning with 0 or 1.

If a new student joined our class, what shoe size would you predict for this student? Why? How does our line plot and discussion help us answer this question?

The topic of shoes offers a wealth of opportunities for many kinds of investigations and extensions. For example, read *How Big Is a Foot?* and discuss the concept of standard versus nonstandard measurement.

Brainstorm a list of attributes for shoes, such as *color, material, kind of fastener,* and *sole pattern.* Ask one child to sort the rest of the children in class according to their shoes, while everyone tries to guess the sorting rule or rules.

How many different ways can we sort ourselves according to footwear?

What other questions can we ask about our shoes? For example, do shoe prints with the same area have the same length? How might we find out?

Are all shoelaces the same length? How are laces sized? What is the relationship between the number of eyelets in a shoe and the length of its lace? How does the width of laces vary? Why? What kinds of materials are used for shoelaces? How might we test the strength of different laces? What prevents laces from unraveling? When did you learn to tie your laces? Could we write a book that helps children learn to tie their laces?

The children might generate a similar list of questions related to other ways to fasten shoes.

What other kinds of fasteners do shoes have? What can we ask about buckles, or buttons, or elastic? What kinds of shoes have no fasteners?

The children may explore shoe-print perimeters, shoe weight, or other attributes. They might be interested in how shoes are made. Invite a shoemaker or a shoe salesperson to class to share what they know about making and sizing shoes.

Teacher Note

Challenge the children to design a new type of footwear for a certain purpose or occasion. How about a special shoe for climbing fences or visiting the library?

Flying Tennis Shoe

Mystery Shoe Print

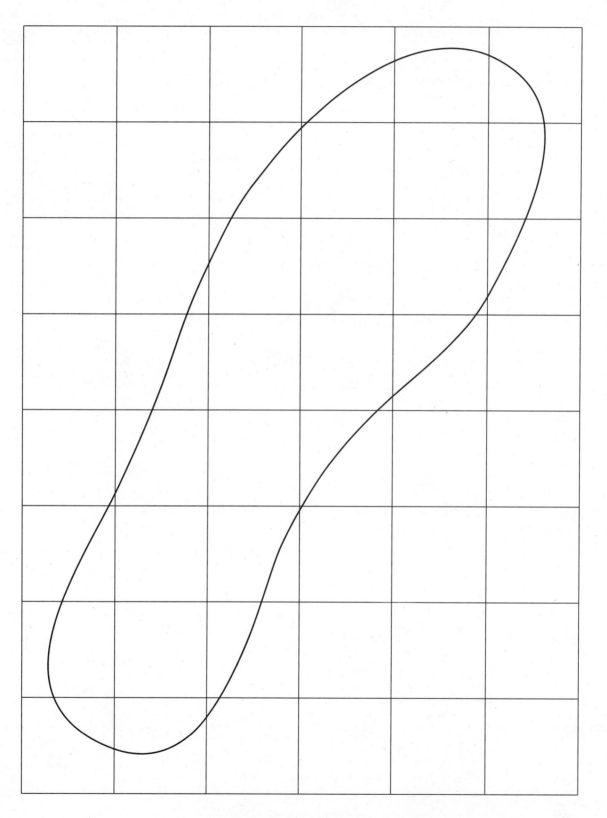

How Many Times Can We Jump Rope?

Mathematical Focus

- comparing, ordering, and counting
- collecting, organizing, and describing data
- comparing two data sets using range, mode, and median
- designing an investigation
- identifying and controlling variables

Materials

- several class lists *(optional; for recording children's jumps)*
- clipboard and pencil *(optional)*
- stick-on notes
- jump ropes and/or plastic hoops
- large sheets of graph paper *(1 for each collection of data)*

Connections

Science
- identifying and controlling variables

Literature
- *Jump Rope!* by Peter L. Skolnik (New York: Workman Publishing, 1974)
- *Statistics* by Jane Jonas Srivasta (New York: Thomas Y. Crowell, 1973)
- *Jump the Rope Jingles* by Emma Vietor Worstell (New York: Collier Books, 1961)

When children jump rope, they naturally count jumps and compare the counts from jumper to jumper or keep track of personal records. They also have different jumping styles: some jump with both feet at once, while others skip by lifting first one foot and then the other.

This investigation extends the children's experience with jumping rope by introducing the control of variables, such as the kind of rope used. The children will collect two sets of data, make representations of both sets of data, and then compare the data sets in various ways.

Posing the Question

Start a discussion with the children about what they might investigate about jumping rope.

What do we want to know about our jumping? For example, can "two feet" jumpers jump more times than "skip" jumpers? Do we jump better when wearing sneakers than when wearing other kinds of shoes? How do our "hot pepper"—or very fast—jumps compare to our regular jumps? Can we jump more times using a plastic hoop, or a rope?

Help the class select a question to begin the investigation. You might want to avoid questions that set up intense competition between individuals; consider trying to sway competitions toward a team approach.

Can taller people jump more times than shorter people? How will we define taller and shorter? Can girls jump more times than boys?

If you think the children need to begin with two sets of data that have equal numbers, you might decide to begin with a question like whether the type of shoes or the jumping tool make a difference. This way, each child jumps twice, once while wearing sneakers (or using a plastic hoop) and a second time wearing other shoes (or using a rope). An advantage to beginning with data sets of equal size is that the two data sets may first be compared simply by comparing the total number of jumps.

Fun Facts

Historical evidence suggests that jumping rope is probably ancient, predating the 1600s, and was originally a boy's game. Today, many people jump rope, including ball players, boxers, and cardiac patients.

Extensions

- The children might be interested in learning more about jump-rope games. *Jump Rope!* is a useful resource of jumping games, terms, and rhymes. Double Dutch jumping has developed to the point that national team competitions are held annually. These competitions are entertaining to watch because of the rhymes and gymnastics.
- Ask the children to recite the jumping rhymes they know, and read them some new ones. (Some traditional jumping rhymes are included in "Rope Rhymes.") What do the rhymes have in common? Challenge the children to write new jumping rhymes.

If the children are at a more advanced level, you can help them discover the usefulness of measures of center, such as median and mode, by selecting a question that will result in data sets of unequal size. For example, questions about differences between boys and girls in your class, or comparisons of two different classes, will probably result in data being collected from groups of different sizes.

Collecting the Data

What do we need to decide about collecting our data? Do we need any special rules to make sure our data helps us to answer our question?

As the children discuss ways to make the jumping "fair" for everyone, they are really talking about how to control variables. For example, if the children believe that the length of the rope makes a difference, they will probably decide that everyone should use the same rope.

The class needs to decide who will jump, who will count the jumps, and how the counts will be recorded. After the rules, or controls, are agreed upon, the children jump rope and record data.

Keeping track of stick-on notes might be difficult if the class collects the data outdoors. It might be useful to duplicate several class lists, and clip them to a clipboard with a pencil. After the children have recorded their data on paper, they could transfer the data to stick-on notes back in the classroom, since stick-on notes are so easy to use for organizing data.

Analyzing the Data

Help the children create two line plots (in close proximity to facilitate comparisons) by arranging each data set in order from the lowest number of jumps to the highest. They can do this by arranging the pieces of data to the wall, in order from left to right.

If the two data sets are equal in number, begin the discussion with a simple comparison of the numbers.

What is the smallest number on each line plot? What is the greatest number on each line plot?

Depending upon the children's previous experience, you may want to continue this discussion by focusing on the general shape of the data.

When we look at a display of data, one of the first things we might notice is its spread, or range. How much distance is there between the smallest number and the largest number?

Are the data close together in a clump, or are they spread out? Are there pieces of data that seem to be separated from others at either end? Will someone volunteer to come to the graph and point these out? Pieces of data that are not close to the other data in a set are called outliers.

From the Classroom

A student in Wendy Rich's class suggested the investigation of jumping rope. Wendy's class began with the question, How many times can we jump rope? Her students raised many issues about how the data should be collected. They decided that they all needed to use the same rope to make things fair. They also set up these additional controls: two people counted to make sure no one cheated, each person had a practice round, and everyone jumped with feet together. Later, students realized that they could answer other questions with the information they had collected.

Next, we might notice bumps, or high spots, where the data is clumped together. These are the numbers of jumps that the greatest number of students completed.

The number that appears most frequently is called the mode. (It is possible to have more than one mode. For example, nine children may have jumped 17 times and nine may have jumped 18 times.)

We might want to find the middle value in the display. This is called the median.

Interpreting the Results

How does our data help answer our question? Are there any other questions we can answer with our data? What else would we like to know about our jumping?

Rope Rhymes

Teddy Bear, Teddy Bear, turn around
Teddy Bear, Teddy Bear, touch the ground
Teddy Bear, Teddy Bear, shine your shoe
Teddy Bear, Teddy Bear, that will do
Teddy Bear, Teddy Bear, go upstairs
Teddy Bear, Teddy Bear, say your prayers
Teddy Bear, Teddy Bear, turn out the light
Teddy Bear, Teddy Bear, say goodnight
Teddy Bear, Teddy Bear, hop on one foot,
    one foot
Teddy Bear, Teddy Bear, hop on two feet, two
    feet
Teddy Bear, Teddy Bear, hop on three feet,
    three feet
Teddy Bear, Teddy Bear, hop right out

Charlie Chaplin went to France
To teach the ladies how to dance.
First on heels,
Then on toes,
Around and around and around she goes.
Salute to the King
And bow to the Queen,
And turn your back on the sour sardine.

A was an apple pie
B bit it
C cut it
D dealt it
E eats it
F fought for it
G got it
H had it
J joined it
K kept it
L longed for it
M mourned for it
N nodded at it
O opened it
P peeped in it
Q quartered it
R ran for it
S stole it
T took it
V viewed it
W wanted it
XYZ and ampersand

All wished for a piece of land.

(Source: Skolnik, Peter L. *Jump Rope!* New York: Workman Publishing, 1974.)

How Often Do We Wear Hats?

Mathematical Focus

- sorting and classifying
- grouping and counting
- collecting, organizing, and describing data
- creating real circle graphs
- predicting
- defining terms

Materials

- 4 index cards
- 4 long pieces of string or yarn
- chair
- large paper circle (optional)

Connections

Technology
- designing a new hat

Literature
- *A Three Hat Day* by Laura Geringer (New York: Harper Collins, 1985)
- *Anno's Hat Tricks* by Akihiro Nozaki and Mitsumasa Anno (New York: Philomel, 1984)
- *The 500 Hats of Bartholomew Cubbins* by Dr. Seuss (New York: Random House, 1965)
- *Caps for Sale* by Esphyr Slobodkina (New York: Harper Collins, 1987)
- *A Hat So Simple* by Jerry Smath (Mexico: BridgeWater Books, 1993)

This investigation might be launched with a special hat day when everyone wears a hat to school. This is an opportunity to capitalize upon young children's enjoyment of doing something unusual.

The children begin the investigation by gathering data about how often they wear a hat, and then they ask more questions about wearing hats. This lesson provides an opportunity for them to represent data in the form of a circle graph at a concrete level.

Posing the Question

Plan time for the children to share personal stories about their hats and when they wear them.

What kinds of hats do you wear? When do you wear them? Is there anyone here who never wears a hat?

Collecting the Data

How often do you wear a hat?

Write the following categories on the board: "Often," "Sometimes," "Seldom," "Almost Never or Never." It might be helpful to combine symbols with the words. For example, use a filled-in hat to represent "Often," a two-thirds-filled hat to represent "Sometimes," a one-third-filled hat for "Seldom," and an outline of a hat for "Almost Never or Never."

If we sort ourselves according to these categories, which group do you think will be the largest? [Juan] says he isn't sure because he's not sure what we mean by "sometimes." What do you think?

When the children seem comfortable with their definitions for the categories, have them line up according to how often they wear a hat. Hand the first person in each line an index card with a picture or label for that category.

If the children wear hats to school for a special hat day, you can use the occasion for other activities. Brainstorm a list of hat attributes and have the children sort themselves by those attributes. Ask the children to tell all the different names they know for hats, such as *cap, bonnet, helmet, beret,* and *turban.* Ask them to define *hat.* Explore how hats are sized. What is the relationship between head circumference and hat size?

From the Classroom

Lisa Williamson uses rolls of toilet paper to section off these circles of students. The rolls sit in the center of the circle and the first person in each category holds on to the paper streamer coming off the roll.

Extension

Read *A Hat So Simple,* and show the children how to make a simple hat. The next day, have the children bring decorations or useful add-ons to attach to their simple hats. You might want to challenge the children to design a hat that will attract birds or one that would be useful throughout the school day or at night.

Real Bar Graph

Analyzing the Data

Which category is the largest? Which is the smallest? How does this compare to our predictions?

Now we are going to rearrange ourselves into a different kind of graph, a circle graph.

Help the children get into a tight circle—shoulder to shoulder—while staying with their category. Place a chair in the center of the circle. Anchor four long pieces of yarn or string to the chair, and hand the loose ends to the children holding the category cards. This divides the circle into four sections, or sectors, one for each category.

Real Circle Graph

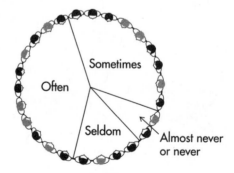

You might carry the children's representation a step further by placing a paper circle in the center of the circle of children. The paper circle can be any size, as long as its center is over the center of the student circle. Draw lines radiating out from the center of the paper circle that line up with the lengths of yarn (these are *radii* of the paper circle). Label each sector appropriately. The paper circle is a more abstract representation of the real graph created by the children.

Interpreting the Results

What can we say about how often we wear hats? Does our graph tell us when we wear hats? Can we tell what kind of hats we wear? Can we tell how we compare to other groups? What else would we like to know?

Some further investigations might involve gathering data about other groups.

Do sports fans wear hats more often than other people? Do older people wear hats more often than younger people? Which occupations involve wearing a hat? Do most occupations require hats, or not?

Extension

The mathematics of combinations can be explored through the hat theme. Read *A Three Hat Day*, and ask the children how many different combinations of hats R. R. Pottle could wear on a three hat day. The children might stack interlocking cubes to represent these different combinations (actually, these are *permutations*, because R. R. Pottle wears his hats in a specific order). *Anno's Hat Tricks* carries this concept even further.

From the Classroom

Jeane Joyner talked to her students about people wearing wigs during George Washington's era. She asked each student to draw a picture of his or her head on a large index card, oriented vertically. Then she asked if they would have liked to have worn a wig during George Washington's time.

The first time Jeane did this activity, she let students who answered yes

to her question glue cotton balls on their pictures to show their wigs. She was surprised to find that almost everyone answered yes. During a class discussion, she realized that the students' choice was influenced by their desire to glue something onto their self-portraits.

The next time she posed the question, to a different group of students, Jeane told them they would glue

cotton balls to show wigs and the appropriate color of yarn to show no wigs. This produced a more balanced set of data based on preferences related to wig wearing rather than to gluing something to an index card. Her students were then ready to discuss the advantages and disadvantages of wearing a wig.

Susan—wig

Paul—no wig

What's Our Opinion?

Mathematical Focus

- designing a survey
- collecting, organizing, and describing data
- choosing appropriate data displays
- connecting surveys and polls to decision making

Materials

- variety of grid paper *(for making graphs; see pp. 109–111)*
- "My Favorite Things" survey *(optional)*
- "Student Census" survey *(optional)*
- database software *(optional)*
- "Mystery Graphs" *(optional)*

Connections

Communication Skills
- finding and reading results from opinion polls and surveys

Literature
- *The Wolf's Chicken Stew* by Keiko Kasza (New York: G. P. Putnam's Sons, 1987)

Opinion polls and surveys are frequently quoted in the news, and they are used by marketing researchers to help businesses make decisions about products and services. This investigation engages children in designing and conducting opinion polls and surveys.

The children begin by brainstorming a list of questions related to conducting opinion polls. They choose one of their questions, and then collect, organize, represent, and interpret the data needed to answer it.

Posing the Question

The best way to introduce this investigation is by asking the children their opinion about a relevant and pertinent classroom or school issue—for example, what to name a new class pet or which new books to add to the school library. If these opportunities don't exist, ask the children about their favorite things (see the "My Favorite Things" survey).

What is your favorite school subject?

As the children share their answers to this question, write them on the board.

Suppose we wanted to find out about people's favorite things. What other favorites could we ask about? Are you interested in knowing about people's favorite books, hobbies, or after-school activities?

List children's ideas on the board. This might be an appropriate time to read aloud *The Wolf's Chicken Stew*. The wolf's favorite number is 100, and he has many favorite scrumptious foods.

Collecting the Data

Of all the ideas we have come up with, which questions should we ask?

Encourage the children to select four or five questions. More than five questions might be unmanageable during the analysis. The children may decide to ask just one question, such as, What is your favorite scrumptious food? or, What is your favorite book?

Now that we have chosen our questions, we must decide who we are going to ask. Should we ask students in other classes or grade levels? Should we ask our families or other people at school?

Once this decision has been made, talk about how to collect and record the data. If children are nonreaders, their questionnaire will need to have pictures for the categories.

Do we need some kind of form or questionnaire?

"My Favorite Things" and "Student Census" are sample question-naires that the children can look at if they decide to develop a survey. Or, they may decide to ask their questions in person and write the answers on a piece of paper.

How will we make sure we don't interview the same person twice?

This may or may not be an issue, depending upon the plan for collecting the data.

Ask questions about biasing samples.

If we ask only boys, only girls, or only students in second grade about their favorite toys, what happens to our data?

Make sure everyone agrees on the questions to be asked and how they will proceed before they collect the data.

Analyzing the Data

Once all the data have been collected, talk with the children about how to analyze the information. Other activities in this book offer opportunities for children to learn how to create a variety of data displays. As you talk with the children, use terms with which they are familiar.

How can we organize our data? What are some ways to represent our data? Can we use a pictograph, a bar graph, or a line plot?

If the children have conducted a survey of favorite things, you might choose to introduce a database program if one is available at your school. Data gathered from a single questionnaire or a survey can be entered into the database. Alternatively, the children could create their own data-collection method by storing forms in a binder in alphabetical order. The collection could be searched for specific information and updated whenever needed.

If the children have asked, say, five questions, divide the class into five groups and have each group analyze a different question. This will probably result in different kinds of representations, ranging

From the Classroom

Mary Anne Auer, a media specialist, asked the students in her school to vote for the books they wanted added to the school library. She selected seven to ten award-winning books for each grade level. She then invited classes to visit the library, where she displayed the books on special carts for a week so students could look through them and make choices. The children had an opportunity to vote for their favorite two or three books at their grade level, and the winning selections were added to the library.

from pictographs to charts. Have each group share their results and representation with the class. Lead a discussion about the appropriateness of each representation.

Why is a [line plot] one good way to represent data about a favorite [school subject]?

Interpreting the Results

What did we learn from our survey? If a new student joined our class, could we predict his or her favorite [school subject]? How could we use this information? Do you think anyone else would be interested in our data? Why?

If appropriate, act upon the children's survey or poll. For example, if the children have collected data on naming a new class pet, name the pet the most popular choice (assuming it is appropriate). If the children have gathered information about new books for the school library, pass their ideas along to the media specialist.

Extension

Most children enjoy solving mysteries. Have children work in pairs to discuss all the possible questions the two "Mystery Graphs" (see pages 74 and 75) might answer, add labels to the graphs, and justify their ideas. Challenge the children to create their own mystery graphs.

My Favorite Things

We are collecting information about some of your favorite things.
There are five categories. Please list one choice in each category.
Make sure they are your favorites!

1. My favorite food: _____

2. My favorite pet: _____

3. My favorite after-school activity: _____

4. My favorite school subject: _____

5. My favorite book: _____

Thank you for your time!

We are collecting information about some of your favorite things.
There are five categories. Please list one choice in each category.
Make sure they are your favorites!

1. My favorite food: _____

2. My favorite pet: _____

3. My favorite after-school activity: _____

4. My favorite school subject: _____

5. My favorite book: _____

Thank you for your time!

Student Census

Name _____

               first   middle   last

Date of birth _____ Age _____

            month   day   year

Address _____

           street   city   state   zip code

Telephone number _____

Where were you born? _____

How many people live at your address? _____

How many brothers do you have? _____

How many sisters do you have? _____

What color is your hair? _____

What color are your eyes? _____

Are you left-handed or right-handed? _____

Which grades have you attended at this school? _____

How do you usually come to school? *(circle one)*

car   bus   walk   bicycle   other _____

Which of these subjects is your favorite? *(circle one)*

reading   math   science   social studies

Which of these is your favorite activity? *(circle one)*

playing   watching TV   reading   other _____

Mystery Graph 1

What questions could this graph be answering? Why? How would you label this graph? Give this graph a title and labels.

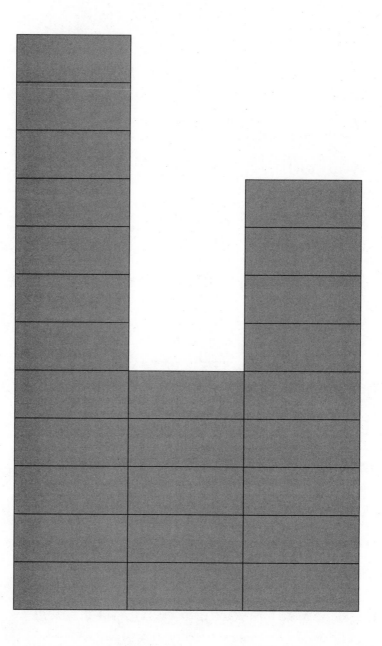

Mystery Graph 2

What questions could this graph be answering? Why? How would you label this graph? Give this graph a title and labels.

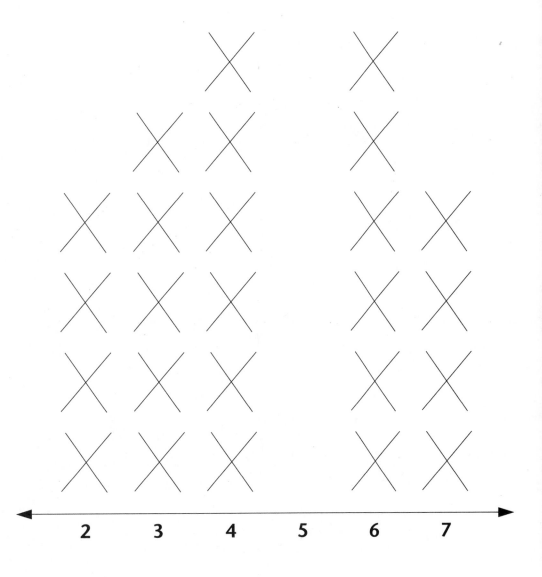

What's Our Favorite Kind of Donut?

Of all the opinions and preferences we have, those about food are some we share most often. One way to investigate food preferences is to find out not what people say they eat, but to gather evidence of which foods are actually eaten.

This investigation requires some special supplies and equipment. You will need an electric frying pan, a spatula or fork, and vegetable oil. Purchase an inexpensive brand of canned biscuits (not the flaky variety). Fill three brown paper bags with coatings for the donuts: cocoa and powdered sugar (or hot chocolate mix), granulated sugar and cinnamon, and plain powdered sugar.

The children will choose one of four kinds of donuts to make: plain, cocoa, cinnamon, or powdered sugar. They will create a real graph, a pictorial representation, and a symbolic graph representing their choices. (Before conducting this activity, please check that none of the children is diabetic or has allergies or other dietary concerns, and adjust the activity accordingly, such as using plain cinnamon or unsweetened cocoa with sugar substitute as toppings.)

Posing the Question

What is your favorite kind of donut? Today we will investigate which of four kinds of donut—cinnamon, cocoa, powdered sugar, and plain— is your favorite.

Collecting the Data

Distribute napkins and paper plates, and ask the children to write their names on them. While the rest of the class is working on other tasks, have a small group of children wash their hands. Demonstrate how to make a hole in the middle of a canned biscuit.

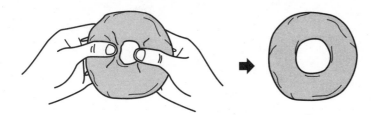

Mathematical Focus

- grouping and counting
- collecting, organizing, and describing data
- moving from concrete to more abstract data representations
- generating new questions

Materials

- electric fry pan and fork or spatula
- vegetable oil, powdered sugar, granulated sugar, cinnamon, and cocoa
- 3 paper bags
- canned biscuits *(enough for 1 biscuit per child)*
- napkins
- small paper plates *(1 per child)*
- crayons
- glue or stapler
- graphing mat *(see "How to Make Graphing Mats" on p. 5)*
- chart paper *(optional)*

Connections

Literature
- *Chicken Soup with Rice* by Maurice Sendak (New York: HarperCollins, 1962)
- *Stone Soup* by Marcia Brown (New York: Macmillan, 1947)
- *Mr. Rabbit and the Lovely Present* by Charlotte Zolotow (New York: Harper and Row, 1962)

Then you will fry the "donut" on both sides in vegetable oil. (Careful: hot oil can splatter!)

Each of you will choose a coating for your donut, shake your donut in the paper bag containing that coating (or leave your donut plain, if that's your favorite kind), and place it on your napkin. Then, on your paper plate, color a donut that looks like your real donut.

They may take a bite or two while waiting for the next step, but remind them not to eat the whole donut—they will need at least part of it to make a real graph of the donuts.

Analyzing the Data

How many of each kind of donut have we made?

Help the children place their donuts on a graphing mat labeled "Powdered sugar," "Cocoa," "Cinnamon," and "Plain."

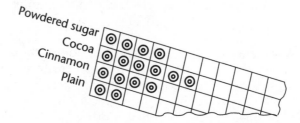

Now, how can we arrange our paper-plate donuts to show the same information?

Paper plates are light enough to be easily attached to a bulletin board to create a pictorial representation. The children can staple the paper-plate donuts to a bulletin board or glue them to chart paper to make a pictorial representation. Help them add appropriate labels.

Depending upon the children's experience, you may choose to have them make a symbolic bar graph of their data. Having the children make a real graph, a pictograph, and finally a symbolic graph helps them to connect concrete experiences with abstract symbols.

Teacher Note

Children do not automatically make connections between concrete experiences and abstract symbols. An important part of creating an environment that assists children in making sense of concepts is bridging from concrete to pictorial to abstract representations.

Favorite Donuts Pictograph

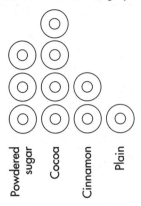

Powdered sugar | Cocoa | Cinnamon | Plain

Favorite Donuts Bar Graph

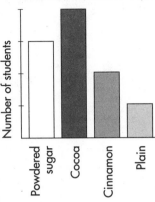

Number of students

Powdered sugar | Cocoa | Cinnamon | Plain

Interpreting the Results

What can we say about our favorite donuts? Is there a class favorite?

If we did this investigation with another class, would the results be the same? Are there other favorite foods you would like to investigate?

Another approach to investigating food preferences is to ask the children to bring food labels from home. The children may decide to investigate favorite soups by collecting soup-can labels or favorite cereals by collecting box tops. They can use their collections to construct pictographs, and then, depending on their level of understanding, the data can be represented in bar graphs.

Extensions

- The children may want to collect data on how many different kinds of donuts local shops make. *Do all the shops make the same kinds? How many different combinations could one eat on a "two-donut day"?*
- Read *Stone Soup,* and ask the children to bring a favorite vegetable to school. They could sort and classify their vegetables by color, shape, and other attributes—then, of course, make stone soup!

From the Classroom

Judy Peede read *Mr. Rabbit and the Lovely Present* to her students and asked them to bring their favorite fruit to school the next day. Students sorted, grouped, and made real graphs of their fruit collection. Finally, they washed and arranged their fruit in a basket and presented it to someone very special—the school's secretary.

From the Classroom

Vicki Moss extended the donut investigation by engaging her grade 3 students in a blind taste test. She called three local donut shops, explained what she was planning, and asked for a donation of one dozen glazed donuts. Vicki marked the donuts as being from donut shop A, B, or C; only she knew which donuts were donated by which shop. Students began by looking closely at a whole donut from each shop. They rated the donuts based on appearance, with 1 as the top rating. They recorded their number 1 choices for appearance in a chart.

Number 1 Choice for Appearance

A	B	C
卌 卌 |||	卌 卌 卌 卌	卌 卌 |||||

Vicki cut the remaining 11 donuts from each dozen into bite-size pieces. Students were asked to divide a napkin into three areas with a crayon and label the areas A, B, and C. Vicki gave each student a part of a donut from shop A, B, and C.

Students tasted the donuts, ranked them, and recorded the rankings on their napkin. They created a second chart of their number 1 choices for taste.

Number 1 Choice for Taste

A	B	C
卌 卌 卌 |||	卌 卌 |||	卌 卌	

Next, her students created a more sophisticated graph by pairing bars for taste and appearance side by side for each donut shop.

Students enjoyed the investigation so much that they conducted taste tests on pizza, chocolate chip cookies, and potato chips before the year ended. Vicki found three pizza restaurants that were willing to donate a 12-inch cheese pizza to the class.

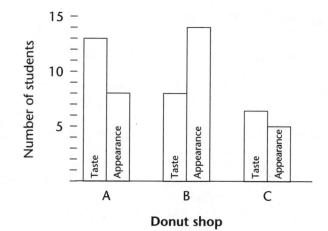

Donut shop

How Old Is Our Money?

Money is a topic of universal interest. Most children have experiences with finding, saving, and spending money. Some may even have their own coin collections.

For this investigation, children gather data on the mint dates of coins they bring to school and create a line plot using stick-on dots to show the dates on their coins. This provides an opportunity for direct comparison and ordering of a small number of items.

Posing the Question

The day prior to posing the question, if possible, read the story *Henry's Pennies* aloud. Henry collects pennies. He finds them under furniture, in his mother's pin dish, and outdoors. He likes the feel of pennies in his pocket and the noise they make when he walks. After the story, lead a discussion about coins.

Have you ever found a coin? Where have you found them? Do you save coins? Where do you keep them?

Ask the children to bring one, two, or three coins to school the next day. Be prepared to loan a few pennies to children without coins. The following day, ask them to lay their coins on their desks.

How old is your money? How can we tell?

Help the children find the dates on their coins. Explain that these dates tell what year the coins were made, or minted.

Can you order your coins from oldest to newest?

Analyzing the Data

Ask questions to find the oldest coin the children have.

Does anyone have a coin minted before 1960? Does anyone have a coin minted before 1970?

Mathematical Focus

- counting and ordering by date
- collecting, organizing, and describing data
- creating a line plot
- finding range, median, and mode *(optional)*

Materials

- children's coins
- extra coins
- chart paper
- stick-on dots *(about 3 per child)*

Connections

Literature
- *Arthur's Funny Money* by Lillian Hoban (New York: Harper and Row, 1981)
- *Dollars and Cents for Harriet* by Betsy Maestro and Giulio Maestro (New York: Crown, 1988)
- *Henry's Pennies* by Louise McNamara (New York: Franklin Watts, 1972)
- *Alexander, Who Used to Be Rich Last Sunday* by Judith Viorst (New York: Atheneum, 1978)

Teacher Note

Depending upon the level of the children, you may decide to have each child use only one coin for the line plot.

Draw a horizontal line on chart paper, and write the date of the oldest coin at the left end.

<--->
|
1968

Ask similar questions to find the most recent mint date.

Does anyone have a coin minted this year? Does anyone have a coin minted last year?

Complete the horizontal axis of the line plot by writing all the years from the earliest to the most recent.

<------|---|---|---|---|---|---|---|---|---|---|---|---|---|---|---|---|---|---|---|---|---|---|---|---|---|---|---|-->
1968 69 70 71 72 73 74 75 76 77 78 79 80 81 82 83 84 85 86 87 88 89 90 91 92 93 94 95

Distribute stick-on dots, and ask the children to write the date of each of their coins on one dot. Help the children place their dots above the axis to indicate the dates on their coins.

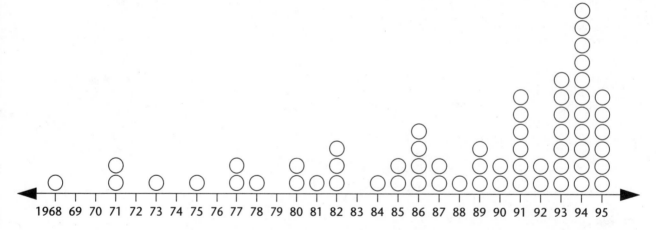

If the children have not had experiences with range, median, and mode, help them to understand these terms. The range is the difference between the earliest and the most recent dates on the coins. Since the median is the middle value, it is helpful with younger children to have an odd number of data. The mode is the date that has the most pennies.

What is the earliest date we have? What is the most recent or latest date we have?

What is the range of our data? What is the median? Do we have a mode?

Interpreting the Results

What can we say about the age of our coins? If we looked at a specific kind of coin—like pennies or silver dollars—would we get similar results?

What else can we ask about coins?

The children can do lots of other coin investigations. For example, younger children could collect data on the number of coins carried by those at home by counting the number of coins in each family member's pocket, purse, or wallet. They could collect data about the dates of coins in the possession of other members of their families, which would give them experience with a larger data set.

You might ask the children to sort their coins by their value—pennies, nickels, dimes, or quarters. The children could work in small groups to investigate dates or total numbers of these sets of coins. This would provide opportunities for comparing data sets.

Are our nickels older than our pennies? Do we have more quarters than pennies?

Fun Facts

- The first coin minted in the United States was a silver dollar. It was issued on October 15, 1794.
- A quarter has 119 grooves on its circumference. A dime has one fewer. You might tell the children this fact, then ask, *Do all coins have grooves? What is the purpose of the grooves?*
- America once issued a five-cent bill.
- If a coin bears the letter *D,* it was minted in Denver; an *S* indicates it was minted in San Francisco; no letter indicates it was minted in Philadelphia.

(Sources: Louis, David. *Fascinating Facts.* New York: Crown Publishers, 1977. Louis, David. *More Fascinating Facts.* New York: Crown Publishers, 1979.)

From the Classroom

Four groups investigating the dates of pennies in their possession found the following when analyzing their data. One group had a range of dates from 1961–1994, with a mode of 1994 and a median of 1988. The second group had a range of 1962–1994, with a mode of 1994 and a median of 1989. The third group had a range of 1959–1994, with a mode of 1994 and a median of 1989. The fourth group found a range of 1968–1994, with a mode of 1994 and a median of 1990. The total number of pennies in these four sets of data were 71, 70, 74, and 73, respectively. It is interesting that all four groups found the same mode. You might want to compare your class's data with these and discuss possible explanations for differences and similarities.

From the Classroom

Data collection and representation are great ways to involve the community in mathematics education and to gather lots of interesting data for children to analyze. Post graphs at family meetings and special events—such as open houses and family math fairs—and invite everyone to add data to them. Graphs can also be posted in common areas, such as the lunchroom or halls, with invitations to other classes or grades to enter data on them. Community graphs can be created with stick-on notes, stick-on dots, tally marks, or Venn diagrams.

Our Birth Months   name = 1 person

January	Bill, Jeff, John, Tim
February	Ann, Mary
March	Kay, Lin, Jane, Tom, Dan, Jim, Abe, Lon
April	Rob, Pat
May	Pete, Jo, Jose, Tim
June	James, Scott, Bob
July	Craig, Laura, Deb, Alan, Dave
August	Rex, Amy
September	Bill, Stu, Pam, Joe, Sam, Tony, Jen, Fay
October	Sue, Meg, John, Amy, Bob
November	Gary, Rosa, Ruby, Tom
December	Pam, Joel, Sam

Favorite Primary Color

Red	Blue	Yellow
𝍸𝍸𝍸𝍸𝍸 𝍸𝍸𝍸𝍸𝍸 |||	𝍸𝍸𝍸𝍸𝍸 𝍸𝍸𝍸𝍸𝍸	𝍸𝍸𝍸𝍸𝍸 𝍸𝍸𝍸𝍸𝍸 |||

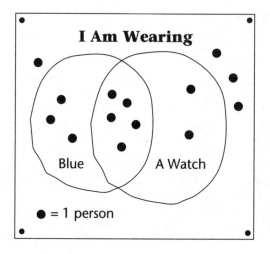

I Am Wearing

Blue   A Watch

● = 1 person

Why Are There Fewer Red Crayons in the Used-Crayon Box?

Mathematical Focus

- sorting, grouping, and counting
- collecting, organizing, and describing data
- making real and abstract circle graphs
- comparing two sets of data to draw conclusions

Materials

- crayons *(several in each of 5 or 6 different colors)*
- containers *(to hold the crayons; empty frozen-juice containers work well, because they don't have sharp edges and won't tip over easily)*
- paper or cardboard circle
- string or yarn
- sorting circles *(optional; large loops of yarn or plastic hoops)*
- string
- collection of used crayons
- chart paper *(optional)*

Connections

Science
- mixing colors

Literature
- *How Is a Crayon Made?* by Oz Charles (New York: Simon and Schuster, 1988)
- *Wishes, Lies, and Dreams* by Kenneth Koch (New York: Harper Collins, 1980)
- *Little Blue and Little Yellow* by Leo Lionni (New York: Ivan Obolensky, 1959)
- *Hailstones and Halibut Bones* by Mary O'Neill (Garden City, New York: Doubleday, 1961)
- *The Rainbow Goblins* by Ul de Rico (New York: Warner Books, 1978)

It's hard to imagine a classroom without crayons. In this two-part investigation, children choose their favorite crayon color and collect data about the colors of crayons in the used-crayon box. They arrange themselves into a real circle graph, and then connect this concrete representation to a more abstract graph made with a paper circle. The children also consider relationships between two different sets of data.

Activity A

Posing the Question

You may want to introduce this investigation by reading several selections from *Hailstones and Halibut Bones,* a collection of poems about colors. Each poem is a metaphor comparing a color to a variety of things.

Think about your favorite colors. What colors of crayons do we have in our crayon boxes? Do you have a favorite crayon color?

Collecting the Data

Ask the children to help you sort the crayons by color into the plastic cups. Place the cups, about 2 feet apart, in a row on the floor.

Take a crayon from the cup with your favorite crayon color, and sit down in a row behind that cup.

Once the children are all sitting, explain that they have made a real bar graph.

We call the rows we are sitting in a real bar graph, because we have used real things—our bodies—to make a graph of bars that shows the colors we choose.

Teacher Note

The title of this investigation is based on a question asked by a student in Janice House's class: "Why aren't there ever any *red* crayons in the used-crayon box?"

Fun Facts

- The first box of Crayola crayons was made in 1903. It cost five cents and had eight colors: black, blue, brown, green, orange, red, violet, and yellow.
- In 1993, Crayola crayons came in 112 colors. Some of the new colors were Macaroni and Cheese, Rassmatazz, Timber Wolf, and Tickle Me Pink.
- The average child in the United States will wear down 730 crayons by his or her tenth birthday.
- The 24-crayons box is the most popular size.
- The Crayola color Flesh was renamed Peach in 1969, partly as a result of the civil-rights movement.
- Red and black are the most popular crayon colors, mostly because they are used for outlining.
- It takes between 3 and 5 minutes to make a crayon.
- Binney and Smith, the manufacturer of Crayola crayons, make more than 2 billion crayons and 200 million markers a year.
- If all the crayons made in one year were placed end to end, they would circle the earth four and a half times.

Analyzing the Data

I can easily see how many of each color have been chosen; can you? Is there another way we can organize ourselves so that we can all see how many of each color have been chosen?

Let the class try different arrangements. After they have had time to experiment, encourage them to find a solution in which the whole class can be in a circle. For example, the children might first line up grouped according to the color of crayon they chose. Once the children have formed a line, lead the line into a circle.

We call the circle we are sitting in a real circle graph, because we used our bodies to make a circular graph that shows the colors we choose.

How can we help ourselves remember what our graph looks like?

The children may offer a variety of representations. If they don't suggest making a circle graph on a piece of paper, suggest it yourself. Place a paper circle in the center of the children's circle. Stretch pieces of string or yarn from the center of the circle out between the pairs of children where colors change. Outline the strings with a black marker, and ask the children to color their section, or sector, of the circle with their crayons.

Interpreting the Results

Which crayon color was chosen most often? Which color was chosen least often?

What else can we say about our choices of crayon color?

Activity B

Posing the Question

Show the class a box full of used crayons. Explain where the crayons came from and how long you have been collecting them. Share any other interesting information about the box of used crayons.

Could we use this box of crayons to learn anything about popular crayon colors? How can we find out how many of each color crayon is in the box?

Collecting the Data

Lead a discussion about how many and what kind of categories should be used when sorting the crayons in the box.

Will we include chartreuse in the "green" category? How should we decide?

When the children have agreed upon the color categories, write them on the board or on chart paper. The appropriate color can be used to write each color word. Have the children sort the crayons into these categories.

How will we count the crayons in each group? Should a short stub count the same as one that is almost its original length?

If the children don't think of putting shorter pieces end to end to resemble whole crayons, suggest it. Each fabricated crayon would count as one crayon.

Analyzing the Data

How do we want to represent out data? Should we make a bar graph? Should we make a circle graph?

Both bar and circle graphs would be appropriate. Since the children made circle graphs in Activity A, you might prefer to use circle graphs here to give them a second experience in creating this type of data display.

One way to make a real circle graph with these crayons is to use a large plastic hoop. Place the plastic hoop on the floor, and ask the children to space their sorted crayons, one color at a time, evenly around the perimeter of the hoop. A more abstract representation can be constructed from the real graph by placing a paper circle in the center of the hoop, using string to segment and mark the separate sectors, and having the children color each sector with the crayons that sector represents.

Interpreting the Results

What have we learned about the crayon colors in the used-crayon box? Which color formed the largest group? Which color formed the smallest group?

How do these data compare with those of our favorite crayon colors?

Can you explain why it can sometimes be hard to find a color you want in the used-crayon box? Can you explain why there are so many of some other colors?

If you were packaging eight crayons in a box to sell, which colors would you choose? Why?

The company that makes Crayola crayons has found that the colors used most often in the world are black and red. Is that true in our class? Why do you think these colors are used more than other colors?

This last question can be a good writing topic for older children.

- Crayola has recently introduced Glow in the Dark and Glitter colors. In 1994, they added Magic Scent Crayola crayons. These contain miniature capsules that burst with odor when rubbed on a surface. The 16 scents—cherry, chocolate, licorice, banana, bubble gum, blueberry, coconut, fresh air, grape, lemon, lime, orange, peach, pine, rose, and strawberry—return when the resulting artwork is scratched. Blue cheese, cinnamon, leather, new car, peanut butter, and skunk were rejected by the company.
(Source: Binney and Smith, 1100 Church Lane, P.O. Box 431, Easton, PA 18044.)

 *From the Classroom*

A class was investigating objects for properties of sinking and floating, and decided to test crayons from the used-crayon box. They discovered—much to their surprise—that most colors sank, while purple floated! The teacher decided this would be a good opportunity to investigate density.

From the Classroom

Lorraine Malphurs' grade 2 class had been exploring the season of fall. They used fall colors for weaving mats, created leaf-shaped name tags for their lockers, and made child-size scarecrows and soft-sculpture pumpkins. She decided to capitalize upon their interest in fall colors to investigate statistics.

Lorraine placed five cans of crayons on a table, each containing one color of crayons. She wrote the names of the colors on the board: Brown, Yellow, Purple, Red, Orange. When she asked what the words had in common, students replied, "They are color words" and "They are fall colors." She asked them to think about which color they would choose as their favorite.

The class went to the gym and sat around the big painted circle on the floor, with the cans of crayons in the center. Each student chose a crayon from one of the cans and then sat down again, so there was no order to the colors the children held around the circle. Lorraine asked how the class could arrange themselves so that they could figure out which color was chosen most often. One student suggested putting the cans in different areas of the gym and having everyone sit near the can with their color. Lorraine asked whether they could think of a way to organize themselves in one circle. One student said, "Put the cans in A-B-C order." Lorraine arranged the cans in alphabetical order around the inside of the circle. All students with brown crayons sat near the brown can, and so on around the circle, with the colors in alphabetical order.

When Lorraine asked students how they could remember the results when they returned to their classroom, several students suggested making a graph. Using a large cardboard circle and string, Lorraine made a circle graph by sketching between pairs of students where the color changed. Students colored their sector of the cardboard circle with their crayons.

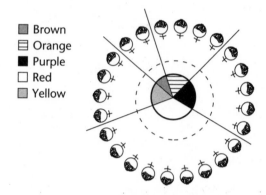

■ Brown
⊟ Orange
■ Purple
□ Red
▨ Yellow

Back in the classroom, students wrote sentences on the circle graph: "Red is our favorite color." "Brown is our least favorite color." "Yellow and orange tied." "Purple is our second favorite color."

Do We Have a Typical Favorite Book?

Mathematical Focus

- sorting and classifying
- counting and ordering
- measuring linear dimensions
- designing survey questions
- collecting, organizing, and describing data
- choosing appropriate data displays
- combining sets of data to describe typical characteristics

Data about our favorite books can help us solve problems such as which books to purchase for the school library or which children's books to publish or sell. It can also be used to create descriptions of what is typical.

"Typical" does not necessarily mean "average." A description of what is typical is composed of a collection of characteristics determined by collecting, analyzing, and interpreting sets of data. For example, one class found that the typical children's picture book contains between 20 and 40 pages, has color illustrations on every page, and is 8 to 12 inches tall.

Materials

- children's favorite books
- graphing mats (see "How to Make Graphing Mats" on p. 5) or sorting circles (large loops of yarn or plastic hoops)
- data-collection materials, such as stick-on notes, grid paper (see pp. 109–111), construction paper, and chart paper
- "My Favorite Book" survey (optional)

Posing the Question

We are going to collect data about our favorite books in order to describe the typical favorite book for our class.

Arrange a special visit to the school library during which the children look for and check out their favorite book. When the children have brought their books back to the classroom, pose the question.

What is your favorite book? Who is the author? What is it about? Does it have pictures? How big or small is your favorite book?

Can we describe the typical favorite book for our class?

Connections

Communication Skills
- using the library

Literature
- *Once Upon a Time . . . Celebrating the Magic of Children's Books in Honor of the Twentieth Anniversary of Reading Is Fundamental* (New York: G. P. Putnam's Sons, 1986)

Collecting the Data

Have the children sort and classify their books using graphing mats or plastic hoops. This experience will prepare them for a more abstract approach to collecting data about their books.

What categories do we want to think about while looking at our favorite books?

Help the children brainstorm possible categories, such as author, topic, number or type of illustrations, number of pages, and size.

Are there any other ways we can group our books?

If you have older children, you may wish to consider more abstract attributes such as those used by libraries.

You might want to introduce this investigation by reading selections from *Once Upon a Time,* a collection of stories and pictures from well-known authors and illustrators of children's books who share their feelings about the relationships they had with books as children. One author confesses that she hid her favorite book in a kitchen drawer so her mother wouldn't be able to return it to the library—she feared it was the only copy in the world! (Reading Is Fundamental is an organization dedicated to bringing good books into the permanent possession of children throughout America.)

Fun Facts

The oldest known books in the world were made of clay and written in cuneiform. They were used for recording land deeds and business transactions by Babylonians 5000 years before movable type was invented in the west.

Do we need to define some of our categories better? Should we provide some choices for themes such as humor, animal, fantasy, adventure, or nonfiction? Should we separate illustrations into color or black and white?

The children should help define the categories. For example, if they want to investigate size, they could determine the dimensions for sorting books into groups such as small, medium, and large. To begin this process, they could first sort a collection of books into three stacks: small, medium, and large. Next, they could assign a range of measurements for height and width to each of the three sizes, based upon the books in each stack.

How will we record the information about our favorite books?

The children may decide to create a form with some choices for each category; see the "My Favorite Book" form. Or they may decide to collect data about each category separately using stick-on notes or another recording approach. Younger children may group the actual books into stacks to make a real graph.

Have each child record the information about his or her favorite book according to the class plan. Some children's books do not have page numbers. If this presents a problem, brainstorm how they might count pages that have no numbers.

Analyzing the Data

How can we organize our data to learn more about our favorite books?

If children have chosen to use a form, divide them into groups and have each group analyze a different set of data. A group analyzing data about the number of pages in each book, for example, may decide to represent the data with a line plot and find the median or mode.

Number of Pages in Our Favorite Books

```
                        X
                        X
        X               X  X                       X
        X       X       X  X          X            X
 X      X  X  X         X  X  X    X  X  X  X    X  X  X     X        X
◄───────────────────────────────────────────────────────────────────►
 19 20 21 22 23 24 25 26 27 28 29 30 31 32 33 34 35 36 37 38 39 40 41 42
```

A group analyzing book titles may decide to count the number of letters or words in each title.

Title	Number of words	Number of letters
The Button Box	3	12
Counting on Frank	3	15
Tuesday	1	7

A group analyzing illustrations may divide the books into three categories according to the artwork they contain—none, black and white, and color—and represent them with a bar graph, pictograph, or chart.

Teacher Note

Making Sense of Data, Addenda Series Grades K–6 (NCTM, Reston, Virginia: 1992) includes a favorite-book investigation for children. The activity begins with the direct comparison of two books and extends to sorting groups of books by size and other attributes. For example, you might hold up two books and ask which is larger. Or, you might ask the children to suggest categories for sorting books, such as which have animals on the cover. After sorting books, the children make real graphs to compare the number of books in each group. Finally, the children create book covers to illustrate their favorite books and display them on a bulletin board.

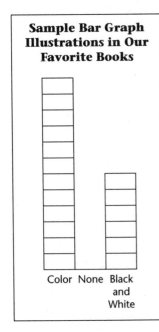

Sample Bar Graph Illustrations in Our Favorite Books

Color / None / Black and White

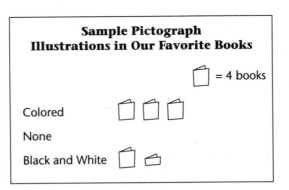

Sample Pictograph Illustrations in Our Favorite Books

= 4 books

Colored

None

Black and White

Sample Chart Illustrations in Our Favorite Books

Colored	None	Black and White

Interpreting the Results

How can we describe the typical favorite book for our class? What can we say about the title? What can we say about the length of the book? What can we say about the size? What can we say about the illustrations? What can we say about the theme?

Help the children design a bulletin board display describing their typical favorite book. This might be a collection of interpretations of each data set in the shape of a book.

The Typical Favorite Book in Our Class . . .

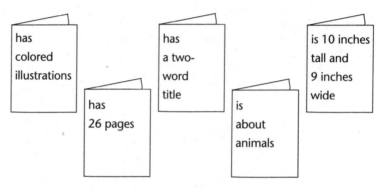

Does your favorite book match the description of our typical favorite book?

Why might an individual favorite book not match all the categories of the typical class favorite?

Invite your school's media specialist to talk to the class about how books are chosen for the library and how they are classified and arranged. If appropriate, the specialist might share information about the Dewey Decimal system, the Library of Congress, and ISBN numbers. If your school is using an automated checkout system, the children might ask questions about what information the system can give them, such as which books are checked out most often.

Are there other typical descriptions we might like to investigate? Could we describe the typical student at our grade level?

My Favorite Book

Title _____

Author _____

Number of pages _____

Size: height _____   width _____

Illustrations (circle one)   color   black and white   none

Theme (circle one)

fiction	nonfiction	animal
fantasy	adventure	humor
poetry	science	how-to
nature	biography	

The PCAI Model for Statistical Investigation

The Teach-Stat project and the activities in this book follow a four-stage model for statistical investigation—the PCAI model (Graham 1987).

Stage 1: Posing the Question

Every statistical investigation begins with a problem or question. Ideally, the problem will be relevant to students' lives, and students should be allowed, as much as possible, to investigate their own problems and questions. Curricular and instructional goals may suggest questions. Even then, activities should encourage intuitive problem solving through exploration. Interdisciplinary connections are another source of questions for students to investigate.

The initial statement of a problem may be vague, and consequently an early step in statistical investigation is to pose more focused, more precise statements of the problem—that is, to refine the question. Question refinement may occur more than once, until a question is formulated that may be addressed by collecting and analyzing data.

Measurements required to address the question are identified at this stage. Both the final form of the question and the types of variables affect how the data are collected, the analysis is performed, and the results are interpreted.

It is essential that students (and teachers) understand clearly how the problem under study relates to specific questions that are eventually asked and variables measured to address these questions. Processes used to formulate focused questions are best acquired through experiences with investigations.

Stage 2: Collecting the Data

The heart of statistics is data. Data are not just a set of numbers; they are a set of measurements. Types of conclusions that can be made from data depend on data-collection design. How to organize data collection depends on the nature of the questions and the variables identified in stage 1.

For many investigations, data will be collected from an entire group. Other questions require that a sample be selected, in which case notions of fairness, randomness, and sample size must be addressed. Cause-and-effect questions must be addressed through data from controlled and comparative experiments. Recording data and measurement errors is also important. Attention must be given to identifying sources of variation in the measurements (for example, inherent differences in the units being measured, the measurement process, or randomness).

As often as possible, students—especially elementary students—should collect their own data. The use of existing data may be appropriate for comparative purposes; however, manufactured data should be avoided.

For example, to explore the typical time people go to sleep at night, a number of teacher educators at a conference were asked, What time did you go to sleep last night? After collecting the times, the teacher educators further refined the question by asking the following questions: How did you decide what time you went to sleep? Did you have any problems answering this question? What kinds of issues would be raised if you tried to clarify the question?

Stage 3: Analyzing the Data

Data analysis focuses on ways to represent data for the purpose of identifying patterns of variation in the data. Students need opportunities for exploration and should be encouraged to create their own representations. Often such representations provide insights into their understanding of the question at hand and how the data relate to that question. There are also several standard statistical representations of data that must be developed. Appropriate representations of data depend on the nature of the questions and the type of data collected. That is, how the data are represented depends on why the data have been collected and what type of data has been collected. Some possible ways to represent the data on times teachers went to sleep are shown on page 97.

Statistical representations of data include graphical displays and numerical summaries. Graphical displays provide visual descriptions of variability in data. Do the data cluster? Are there gaps or unusual values (outliers)? Statistical concepts such as typical or most common value; spread, dispersion, and variability; and shape are easily explored by looking at graphical representations of data. Numerical representations of data provide a means for summarizing conceptual ideas conveyed through graphs.

Stage 4: Interpreting the Results

How do results from the data analysis relate to the original question? Interpreting results requires making sense from the analysis in order to address the questions being asked. Because the interpretation must be communicated either orally or in writing, the results from analysis must be translated from graphical descriptions and numerical summaries into meaningful statements in words.

For example, the following questions might be asked about how to interpret the results shown by the graphs teachers made in an educators' bedtime investigation:

- How would we describe people in this group based on the data we collected?
- If someone walked into this room right now, what might we predict would be the time that person went to sleep last night? Why?
- What can we say about the ways people chose to represent the data?
- How well do the displays summarize the data?
- Are there questions about the representations that were used?
- Can we generalize to all people attending the conference? Why or why not?
- What do we know now?
- What might we want to ask next to refine our understanding of adults' sleeping behavior?

Students need encouragement to be skeptical of their results and to ask critical questions that reveal shortcomings in the previous stages of posing the question, collecting the data, and analyzing the data. Do the questions asked adequately address the problem under study? Are the measurements appropriate for the questions? Have the data been collected properly and measurements recorded accurately? Are data representations appropriate for the questions asked and the data collected? The strength of any conclusions depends on answers to these questions. During this stage, rethinking the original questions and identifying new problems and questions may provide fuel for the process to cycle into another statistical investigation.

Graphs Created by Teachers in a Workshop

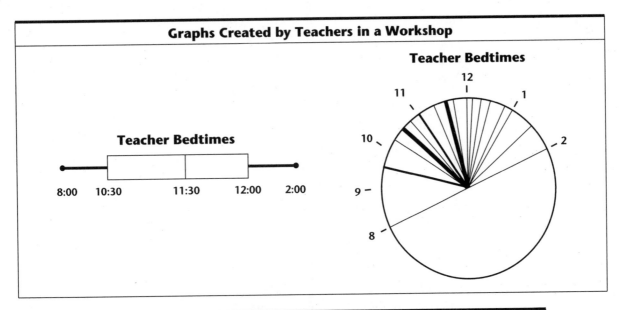

Teacher Bedtimes

Teacher Bedtimes

8:00   10:30   11:30   12:00   2:00

Teacher Bedtimes

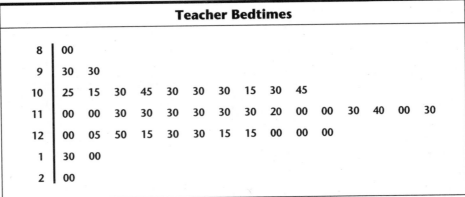

8	00												
9	30	30											
10	25	15	30	45	30	30	30	15	30	45			
11	00	00	30	30	30	30	30	30	20	00	00	30	40	00	30
12	00	05	50	15	30	30	15	15	00	00	00		
1	30	00											
2	00												

Teacher Bedtimes

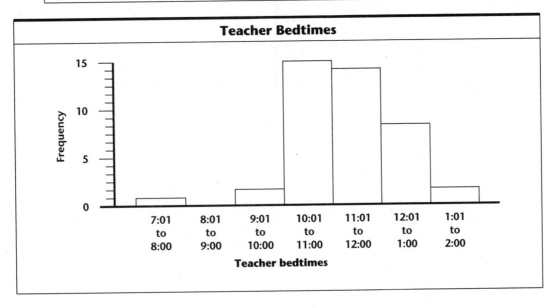

Mapping the Process of Statistical Investigation

The process of statistical investigation may be depicted by a concept map. The center of the map displays the four components of the process of statistical investigation. Attached to each process are related statistical concepts.

- When we *pose the question,* we do so because we want to describe a set of data, summarize what we know about a set of data, compare or contrast two or more sets of data, or generalize from a set of data, making predictions about the next case or about the population as a whole.
- *Collecting data* involves identifying methods for data collection and determining the actual sample or population that will be considered. When sampling is involved, different kinds of samples may be used, including convenience samples or self-selected samples. Instances of bias, representativeness, and randomness become important. The kind of data we collect depends on the nature of the question posed; we need to distinguish among different data types, including categorical and numerical data.

- When we *analyze data,* there are three areas of emphasis: describing the shape of the data; computing descriptive statistics, including mean, median, mode, range, and correlation; and organizing, sorting, classifying, and displaying data using tables, diagrams, and graphs.
- *Interpreting results* leads us back to our question as we reflect on the purpose for our investigation.

References

Crockcroft, W. H. *Mathematics Counts.* London: H.M.S.O., 1982.

Goodchild, S. "School Pupils' Understanding of Average." *Teaching Statistics,* 10 *(3):* 77–81 (1988).

Graham, A. *Statistical Investigations in the Secondary School.* Cambridge: Cambridge University Press, 1987.

Graham, A. *Investigating Statistics: A Beginner's Guide.* London: Hodder and Stoughton, 1990.

Moore, D. S. *Statistics: Concepts and Controversies.* 3d ed. New York: W.H. Freeman, 1991.

Concept Map of the Process of Statistical Investigation

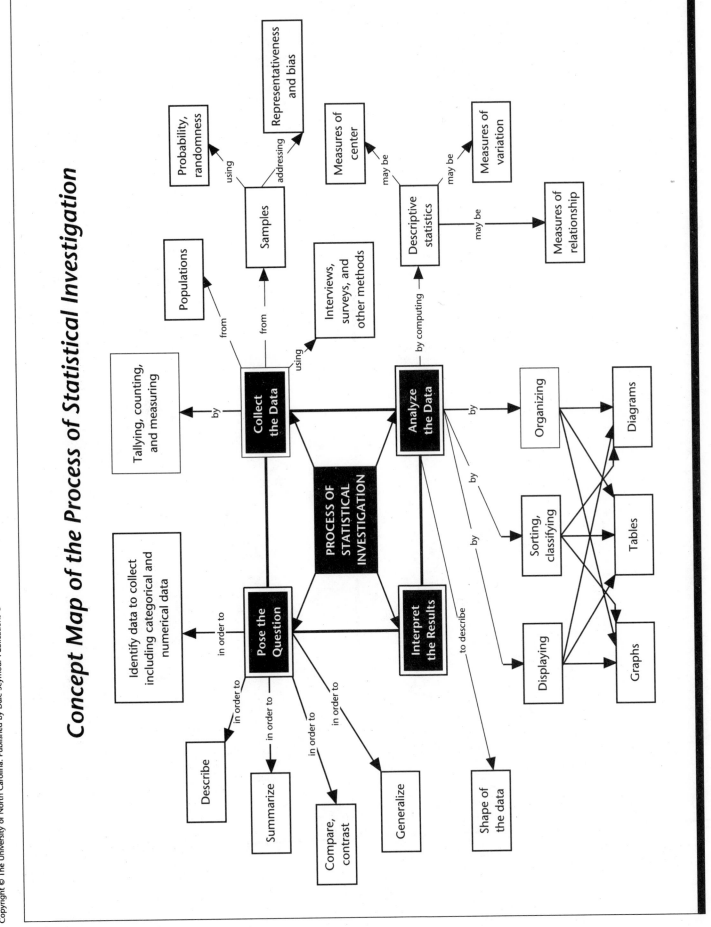

About Statistical Words

Kinds of Data

Data are values such as counts, ratings, measurements, and opinions that are gathered to answer questions. Here are some examples of different kinds of data:

- Height in centimeters of players on the Girls All-American Basketball Team
- Number of people in students' families
- Favorite pizza toppings of teachers

Numerical data are values that are numbers such as counts, measurements, and ratings. Here are some examples of numerical data:

- Numbers of children in families
- Pulse rates of top athletes
- Heights of octogenarians
- Time in minutes that students spend watching television in a day
- Ratings, such as how much people value something (On a scale of 1 to 5, with 1 as "low interest," how would you rate your interest in movies?)

Categorical data are values that often are words and that represent possible responses with respect to a given category. Frequency counts can be made of the values for a given category. Here are some examples of categorical data:

- Months in which people have birthdays (January, February, March, and so on)
- Favorite color t-shirt (magenta, Carolina blue, yellow, and so on)
- Kinds of pets people have (cats, dogs, fish, horses, boa constrictors, and so on)

Continuous data are data that occur on a continuous scale; if you select two values, you can always identify a third value between them. Here are some examples of continuous data:

- Time in minutes it takes for students to travel to school
- Heights in centimeters of students in a class

Discrete data are data for which only certain values are possible; no new value between two certain values can be identified. Here are some examples of discrete data:

- Counts of numbers of people in families
- Numbers of letters in names

Representing Data

A **table** is a tool for organizing information in rows and columns. Tables permit the listing of values and the tallying of the occurrences of each value. A *frequency table* is used to record the number of occurrences of the values within specified intervals; the width or range of each interval is called a *class interval*.

How Many Raisins?	
Raisins in a box	Number of boxes
27	1
28	0
29	2
30	3
31	6
32	2
33	4
34	4
35	2
36	0
37	0
38	0
39	1

Axes are the number lines used to make a graph. There are usually two axes perpendicular to each other (see *bar graph* or *scatter plot* for examples). The vertical axis is referred to as the *y*-axis, and the horizontal axis is referred to as the *x*-axis.

The **scale** of a plot or graph is the size of the unit used to calibrate the vertical axis (and the horizontal axis when the data are numerical). For instance, the vertical axis in the example under *bar graph* represents the frequency of occurrence of names with certain numbers of letters. Each tick mark represents one student. The labels for the tick marks are at intervals of 2, so 2, 4, and so on are labeled.

A **line plot** is a quick, simple method of organizing data along a number line in which Xs (or other symbols) above the number represent the frequency tally of data for that value of the data.

Number of Raisins in Box

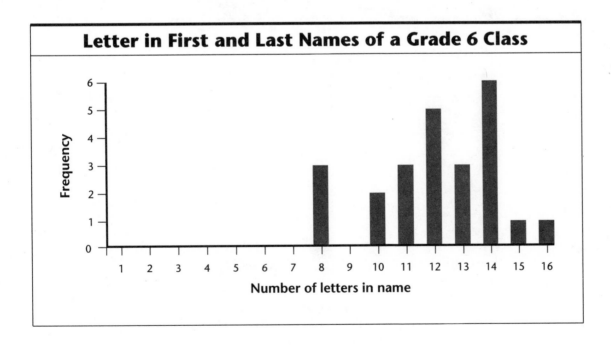

```
                        ×
                        ×
                        ×              ×       ×
                ×       ×              ×       ×
        ×       ×       ×       ×      ×       ×       ×               ×
   ×            ×       ×       ×      ×       ×       ×               ×               ×

   26   27   28   29   30   31   32   33   34   35   36   37   38   39   40
```

Number of raisins

A **bar graph** is a graphical representation of a table of (discrete) data in which the height of each bar indicates its value or frequency. The bars are separated from each other to highlight the discrete nature of the data. The horizontal axis shows the values, and the vertical axis shows the frequency, or tally, for each of the values on the horizontal axis. Bar graphs may be used to display categorical or numerical data.

Letter in First and Last Names of a Grade 6 Class

Number of letters in name

A **histogram** is a graphical representation of a frequency table of continuous data; the height of each bar is the frequency of the variable being graphed. Because of the nature of data, the columns touch. The column widths are generally equal and correspond to the intervals used to group the data. The horizontal axis shows the intervals. A frequency scale on the vertical axis clarifies the meanings of the height of the bars.

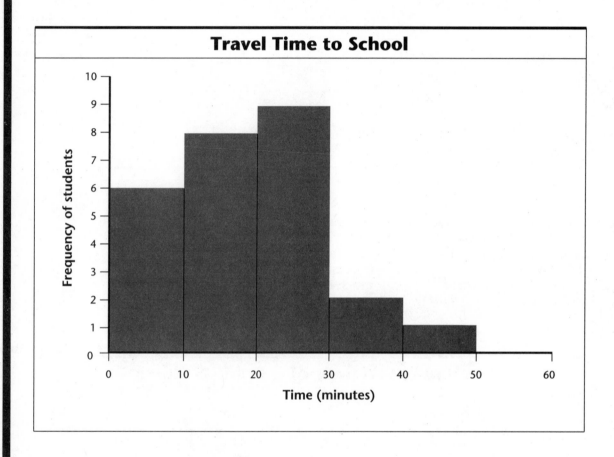

Travel Time to School

A **line graph** is a graphical representation that shows the behavior of a variable over time. The time interval is along the horizontal axis, and the variable is plotted along the vertical axis. Line graphs can be used to identify trends.

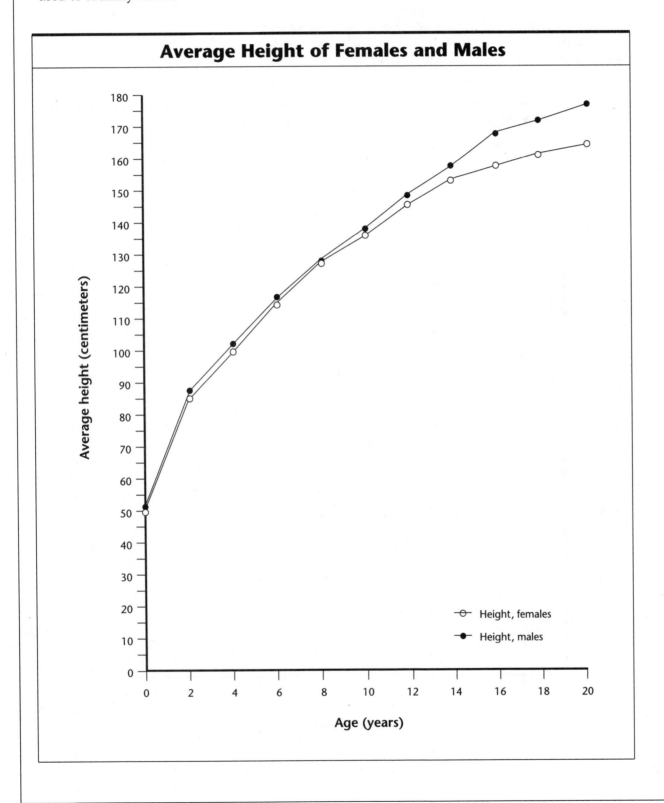

Average Height of Females and Males

A **scatter plot** is a graphical representation of pairs of related numerical values. The data are sorted into pairs of numbers, with each pair associated with one person (for example, height and arm span of the person) or object (for instance, length and width of a rectangle). One axis is designated to show one value of each pair (for example, height on the horizontal axis), and the other axis shows the other value of each pair (for instance, arm span on the vertical axis). The axes of a scatter plot are like those of a coordinate graph.

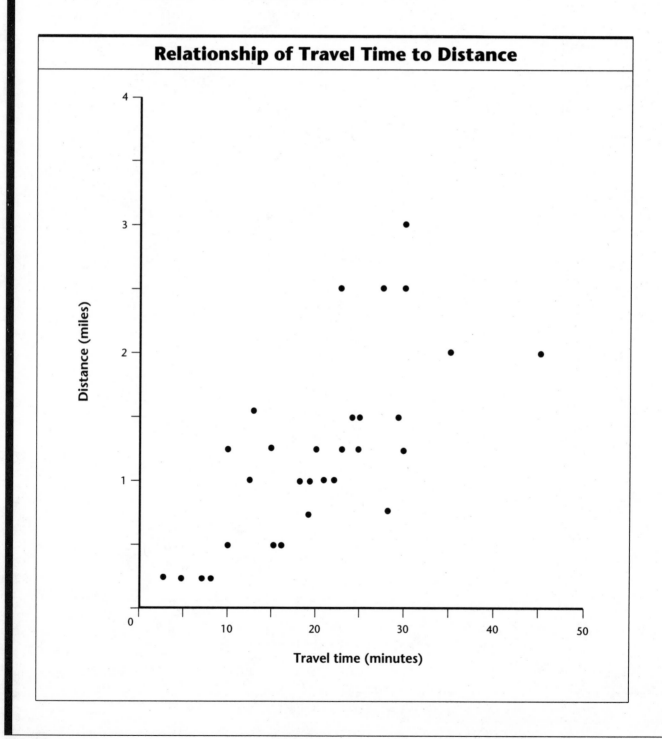

Relationship of Travel Time to Distance

A **stem-and-leaf plot,** or stem plot, is a quick way to picture the shape of a distribution while including the actual numerical values in the graph. The *stem* of the plot forms a vertical number line on the left-hand side that represents a range of values in specified intervals. The *leaves* are the numbers to the right of the stem, they are attached to particular stem values. For example, tens digits are indicated on the vertical axis as the stems, and units digits are next to each tens digit to show the leaves that belong to that stem. *Back-to-back stem plots* may be used to compare two sets of the same kind of data. The units for one set of data are placed on one side of the stem, and the units for the other set of data are placed on the other side of the stem.

Minutes to Travel to School

```
0 | 3 3 5 7 8 9
1 | 0 2 3 5 6 6 8 9
2 | 0 1 3 3 3 5 5 8 8        2 | 3  means 23 minutes
3 | 0 5
4 | 5
```

A **box plot** is a graphical representation that relies on five summary numbers of a data set: the median, the upper and lower quartiles, and the minimum and maximum extremes. Box plots help focus attention on relative positions of different sets of data, making it easier to compare them. They are especially useful when a data set contains hundreds or thousands of numbers. Also, comparisons of data sets with unequal numbers of values do not cause problems with box plots because individual data items are hidden.

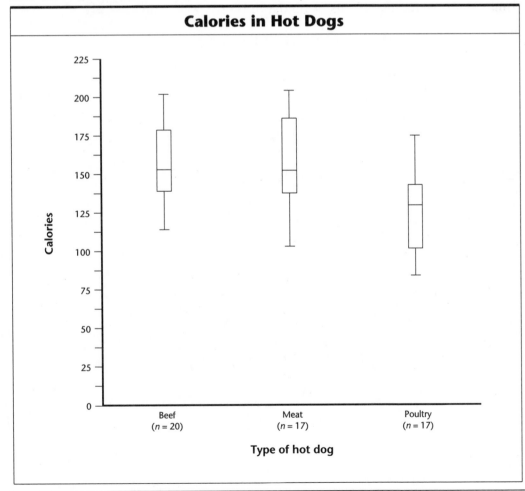

Measures of Center and Variation

The **range** of a distribution is a measure of the spread or variation in the data; it is usually computed by stating the lowest and highest values. Less frequently, the range is computed by finding the difference between the lowest and highest values.

The **mean** of a distribution is a measure of center; it is a value calculated from the data. It can be thought of as the value that a data set would have if all the data were the same value. For example, the mean number of raisins in a box for the distribution (under the entry for table) is $^{802}/_{25}$ raisins, or about 32 raisins. If all 25 boxes had the same number of raisins, they would each have about 32 raisins.

The **median** of a distribution is a measure of center; it is a numerical value that marks the middle of an ordered set of data. Half of the data fall above the median, and half of the data fall below the median. The median of the distribution of raisins (under the entry for *table*) is 32 raisins, because the thirteenth (middle) value in the ordered set of 25 values (27, 29, 29, 30, 30, 30, 31, 31, 31, 31, 31, 31, 32, 32, 33, 33, 33, 33, 34, 34, 34, 34, 35, 35, 39) is 32 raisins.

The mode of a distribution is a measure of center; it is the categorical or numerical value that occurs most often in a data set. For example, the mode of the distribution of the number of raisins (under the entry for *table*) is 31. It is possible to have more than one mode; we talk about data that are *bimodal* (with two modes) and *trimodal* (with three modes).

An outlier in a distribution is a value that lies "outside" of the distribution of the data. There may be more than one outlier in a data set. It is a value that may be questioned because it is unusual or because we wonder whether there was an error in recording or reporting the data. The 39 raisins in the number of raisins (under the entry for *table*) may be considered an outlier.

One-Centimeter Grid Paper

Two-Centimeter Grid Paper

One-Inch Grid Paper